Grammar 5

Activity Sheets

Edited by Amber Densmer

Flip to the back to find extra pages with room to write Notes of your own!

The fear of the Lord is the beginning of knowledge,
But fools despise wisdom and instruction.

Proverbs 1:7 (NKJV)

SONLIGHT
The way you wish you'd been taught.

Sonlight Curriculum® "Grammar 5" Activity Sheets, First Edition

Published by
Sonlight Curriculum, Ltd.
8042 South Grant Way
Littleton, CO   80122-2705
USA
Phone (303) 730-6292   Fax (303) 795-8668
E-mail: main@sonlight.com

NOTE TO PURCHASER

Sonlight Curriculum, Ltd. is committed to providing the best homeschool resources on the market. This entails regular upgrades to our curriculum and to our Instructor's Guides. This guide is the 2010 Edition of the Sonlight Curriculum® Grammar 5 Activity Sheets. If you purchased it from a source other than Sonlight Curriculum, Ltd., you should know that it may not be the latest edition available.

This guide is sold with the understanding that none of the Authors nor the Publisher is engaged in rendering educational services. Questions relevant to the specific educational or legal needs of the user should be addressed to practicing members of those professions.

The information, ideas, and suggestions contained herein have been developed from sources, including publications and research, that are considered and believed to be reliable but cannot be guaranteed insofar as they apply to any particular classroom or homeschooling situation.

The Authors and Publisher specifically disclaim any liability, loss, or risk, personal or otherwise, incurred as a consequence directly or indirectly of the use and application of any of the suggestions or contents of this guide.

Printed in the United States of America.

For the latest information about changes in this guide, please visit **www.sonlight.com/curriculum-updates.html** 🖳. Please notify us of any errors you find not listed on this site. E-mail corrections to *IGcorrections@sonlight.com* and any suggestions you may have to *IGsuggestions@sonlight.com*.

Grammar 5: Sheet 1

Passage

Henry Reed, p. 30:

> By the time we were kids, my folks—that's your grandparents—had sold three lots here on this side of the road. All the present houses were here except that red brick one which you can see over the evergreens. That belongs to Mr. Apple.

F.Y.I.: Being Verbs

Did you know that you can tell what a noun *was, is* or *will be*? Verbs that express a state of being are called **being verbs**. Being verbs require three parts. Match the **bold**, *italics* and underlines in the examples to discover the three parts.

Being verbs require three components:

1. *a noun*
2. **a being verb**
3. one or more words to clarify the noun's state of being.

For example:

Bubba **is** strong.
Lisa **was** laughing.
Zachary **will be** awake soon.

Exercises

Unless directed to do otherwise, mark your answers to these questions on the above passage.

1. Circle the being verbs in the second sentence. Then rewrite the sentence so you don't use any form of the verb **be**.

   _____

   _____

   _____

2. Put check marks above the dashes in the passage above. Why did the author use dashes in this passage?

   ☐ **To indicate interrupted speech**   ☐ **To set off parenthetical material**

   ☐ **For emphasis**   ☐ **To indicate a sudden break**

3. In the second sentence, use an **n** to label the nouns and a **v** to label the verbs. When they are part of a sentence, nouns are often the: **action word**   **person**   **subject**   of the sentence.

   Note: The word "can" is a helping verb, which we will discuss on Activity Sheet 4. Also note that in this context, **one** is a numerical pronoun whose antecedent is the noun **houses**.

4. **Homonyms** are words that sound the same, are spelled the same, but do not mean the same thing. Words such as "wave" (in the sea) and "wave" (to greet) are homonyms. Underline as many homonyms in the passage as you can. Then choose 3 homonyms and write another meaning for each one.

   _____

   _____

⇨ **Sheet 1** *Continued...*

5. **Homophones** are words that <u>sound the same</u>, but do not mean the same thing. Homophones may or may not have the same spelling.[1] Words such as "for" and "four," and "ant" and "aunt," are homophones. Double underline as many homophones in the passage as you can. Then choose 3 homophones and write another meaning for each one.

_____

_____

1. See the *Grammar Guide* in the Resource section for more information.

Grammar 5: Sheet 2

Henry Reed, Inc., p. 44:

"What kind of research are you going to do—pure or applied?" she asked.

"What's the difference?" I asked.

"Well, in pure research you just sort of try and find out things because you're

curious. In applied research you're trying to find the answer to some question."

F.Y.I.: Pronouns

If we hadn't named the book that provided us with today's passage, would you know who was speaking? Perhaps not, since no speaker is ever named in this excerpt. If that's the case, then how do you know that one speaker is female, and that one is the narrator? Pronouns! **Pronouns** take the place of a common or proper noun in a clause or sentence.

In order to write clearly, you must use a common or proper noun before you use a pronoun. This noun then becomes the pronoun's **antecedent**. If you've read this book, you know that "Henry" and "Midge" are the nouns because the author used these names prior to this particular passage. Pronouns must agree with their antecedents in both **person** (1st, 2nd and 3rd) and **number** (singular or plural). For example:

> **Correct:** *Lolly* [3rd/Sing/Fem] bounced into the room and dropped *her* [3rd/Sing/Fem] books on a chair.

> **Incorrect:** The *child* [3rd/Sing/Neut] bounced into the room and dropped *their* [3rd/plural] books on a chair.

Pronouns change forms slightly, depending on how they're used in a clause or sentence. Some pronouns change to relate to their subjects. The chart shows how these pronouns change according to the subject's person and number.

Note: *Nominative* pronouns can express or directly replace the subject of a clause.

Nominative/Subject Pronouns		
Person:	**Number:**	
	Singular	Plural
1st Person	**I** went to school.	**We** went to school.
2nd Person	**You** went to school.	**You** went to school.
3rd Person Masc	**He** went to school.	**They** went to school.
3rd Person Fem	**She** went to school.	
3rd Person Neut	**It** went to school.	

Exercises

Unless directed to do otherwise, mark your answers to these questions on the above passage.

1. Write **n** above the nouns in the second and third paragraphs.

2. A **proper noun** is the name of a *particular* person, place or thing. Proper nouns always begin with a capital letter.

    Write a proper noun for each of the following common nouns:

    school _____   national park _____

    man _____   dog _____

    store _____   mountain _____ ⇨

3. A **common noun** is a general word that refers to a person, place, thing or idea, however common nouns are not named directly. Write a common noun for each of the following proper nouns:

Reverend Smith_____ **Chevy** _____

Empire State Building _____ **Straight Street** _____

San Francisco _____ **Officer Jones** _____

4. Write **pro** above the pronouns in the passage.

5. The last paragraph lacks an attribution. How can you tell who is talking?

   ☐ **You can't.**

   ☐ **You simply "know," because the attribution is "understood."**

   ☐ **Since only two people are talking, and the paragraph changed, you can assume it is the speaker other than the one in the immediately preceding paragraph.**

6. Every sentence has a **subject**—which is always a noun or a pronoun. Subjects are the "who" or "what" the sentence is about. For example:

   Andy climbed the mountain.   **He** launched the football.   The **dog** ate my homework.

   An **implied** or **understood subject** is not directly stated in a sentence, but is still "understood" by the reader. We often use understood subjects when we give commands:

   "Look out!"   or   "Please go clean your room."

   Reread the passage and draw an arrow to the subject (either a noun or a pronoun) that each of the following words modify. If you get stuck, think "Who **asked**?":

   asked   **asked**   **are going**   **try and find**

Grammar 5: Sheet 3

Passage

Henry Reed, Inc., p. 119:

"Where are you going?" I asked.

"Over to call the oil company," she said. "I want to find out how much fuel oil is."

She came back in a few minutes and told me that it was fifteen cents a gallon.

That meant that if we had three hundred gallons we had forty-five dollars worth

of oil. We weren't millionaires but forty-five dollars is a lot more than nothing.

Exercises

1. What three structural features does a complete sentence include? _____

   _____

   _____

2. All sentences should begin with _____ and end with

   _____.

3. Use an **s** to identify the subject in each of the following sentences.

   Where are you going?   ...I asked.   **...call the oil company," she said.**

   I want to find out...   She came...and told...   **...if we had three hundred gallons...**

   Look out!

4. Underline the sentence fragment in the passage.

   What features identify a sentence fragment? _____

   _____

   _____

   Is the sentence fragment in the passage acceptable?   **Yes**   **No**

   Why or why not?

   ☐ **Sentence fragments are just plain wrong.**

   ☐ **It is an author's responsibility to make the people who talk sound as good as possible.**

   ☐ **Dialog does not have to follow normal rules of grammar; it should simply and accurately report what the speaker said.**

5. Draw an X next to the sentence fragments.

    ☐ **Only $19.95!**

    ☐ **I won!**

    ☐ **That I spilled.**

    ☐ **Please hurry.**

    ☐ **Because she slouched.**

    ☐ **Stop!**

6. A **predicate** is anything other than the subject in a clause, and tells you what happened to the subject, what it did, or who it "is." Predicates always contain a verb—in fact, a simple predicate is a verb all by itself. Compound predicates contain two or more simple predicates, and a complete predicate is a simple or compound predicate plus all of their modifiers. Underline the predicates in the clauses below.

    a. Greg sniffed.

    b. Cashew slept the entire time.

    c. He stood up and shouted at the top of his lungs.

    d. Robert's wombats were all the rage.

Grammar 5: Sheet 4

Passage

Henry Reed, Inc., pp. 145-146:

"Who would want a wasps' nest?" Midge asked.

"A museum," I replied.

She didn't think much of the idea, but I asked Mrs. Ainsworth if she minded if I took the wasps' nest. She said certainly not. In fact she would gladly pay me a dollar if I would take it away.

Exercises

1. Draw an arrow from the following subjects to the verbs that modify them:

    Who   **Midge**   **I**   **She**   **I**

    She   **I**   **She**   **She**   **I**

2. **Helping** (or **auxillary**) verbs help form a main verb's mood, tense, or voice, and help to express need, certainty, possibility, and probability. They are often used to ask a question. In the examples below, **auxiliary verbs** are bold; <u>verbs</u> are underlined:

    > **Are** you <u>going</u> to the store?
    > I **might** <u>swim</u> on the team next year.
    > **Do** you <u>think</u> she would **go**?

    Write **hv** over each helping verb in the passage.

3. Write **n** above the common nouns and place check marks above the proper nouns. If you find a word that looks like a noun, but is being used as an adjective (for example, the word **gold** in the phrase **gold ring**), it is not a noun!

4. Write a common noun for each of the following proper nouns:

    Midge _____   **Mrs. Ainsworth** _____

5. Double underline the plural possessive nouns.

6. Underline the sentence fragment.

This page intentionally left blank.

Passage

Henry Reed, Inc., pp. 176-177:

I said, "That culvert's too small anyhow. It gets blocked every time it rains, and floods all the lawns on this side of the road."

"I think there has been a complaint or two about that. Well, I suppose we might just as well put in a larger one while we're at it." He looked at me and grinned. "How big a one would you suggest?"

"Big enough for me to crawl through," I replied.

F.Y.I.: Types of Paragraphs

Did you know that there are four different types of paragraphs? Even though the body of a paragraph will always support its topic sentence, paragraphs can be written in different ways to serve different purposes. Here's a brief description of each of the four types.

Expository Paragraphs: *Just the facts ma'am.*
Expository paragraphs are usually found in encyclopedia articles or informative essays. They present facts, define terms or give instructions.

Descriptive Paragraphs: *Let me paint you a picture.*
Descriptive paragraphs present a clear description of a single person, place, thing or idea. They are filed with information about sights, sounds and smells—details that help the reader experience the scene as though they were actually there.

Narrative Paragraphs: *Here's the story.*
Narrative Paragraphs are often found in newspapers because they tell a story. Details in these paragraphs answer the 5 "W" questions (Who? What? When? Where? and Why?) about a particular event.

Persuasive Paragraphs: *Convincing, aren't I?*
Persuasive Paragraphs express an opinion about a topic, and try to persuade a reader that the opinion is valid. The body of this type of paragraph presents solid evidence to support the main argument.

Exercises

1. Overall, what type of paragraph is this?

   Expository   **Persuasive**   **Descriptive**   **Narrative**

2. Write **n** above the nouns in the first paragraph only.

3. Underline the complete predicate of the second sentence. **Challenge:** What kind of predicate is this?

   A predicate adjective   **A predicate noun**   **A simple predicate**   **A compound predicate**

4. Double underline a compound predicate in the second paragraph.

5. Put slashes between the syllables in the following words: **anyhow**, **every**, **complaint**, **suppose**, **larger**, and **looked**.

6. Identify the verbs that modify these subjects.

I _____   **culvert** _____

It _____ _____   **and** _____

it _____   **I** _____

complaint _____ _____   **I** _____

we _____ _____   **we** _____

he _____ **and** _____   **you** _____ _____

I _____

Grammar 5: Sheet 6

Call it Courage, p. 18:

The boy stood there taut as a drawn arrow awaiting its release. Off to the south somewhere there were other islands…. He drew a deep breath. If he could win his way to a distant island, he could make a place for himself among strangers. And he would never return to Hikueru until he should have proven himself!

F.Y.I.: Types of Sentences

Did you know that sentences fulfill one of four purposes?

Declarative sentences simply state an idea. These sentences usually end in a period, though sometimes they end in an exclamation point. "My, that reeks." and "I think it's time to take out the trash." are both declarative sentences.

Imperative sentences give advice or instructions, make requests, or express a command. "Here, take this." and "Go long!" are imperative sentences.

Interrogative sentences ask direct questions and end with a question mark. "Will you throw that to me?" and "Are you sure you'll catch it?" are interrogative sentences.

Finally, **exclamatory sentences** express strong opinions by making an exclamation. "Yikes!" and "Gross!" are both exclamatory sentences.

Pronouns		
Person/Number	Possessive	
1st/Singular	This is **my** house.	This house of **mine**.
1st/Plural	This is **our** house.	This house of **ours**.
2nd/Singular	This is **your** house.	This house of **yours**
2nd/Plural	This is **your** house.	This house of **yours**.
3rd/Singular Masc	This is **his** house.	This house of **his**
3rd/Singular Fem	This is **her** house.	This house of **hers**.
3rd/Singular Neut	This is **its** house.	
3rd/Plural	This is **their** house.	This house of **theirs**.

Exercises

Use this table to help you with question 4.

1. In the passage, what type of sentence is the first one?   **Imperative   Interrogative   Exclamatory   Declarative**

2. What type of sentence is the last one?   **Imperative   Interrogative   Exclamatory   Declarative**

3. Write the verbs from the passage that go with the following subjects:

   boy _____   **islands** _____

   he _____   **he** _____ _____

   he _____ _____   **he** _____ _____

   he _____ _____ _____

4. Write **pro** above the pronouns. **Hint**: **Himself** and **somewhere** are pronouns.

   Most of the pronouns in today's passage are: **feminine   masculine   neutral**

   Draw check marks above any possessive pronouns.

5. Write **art** above the articles.

6. Authors often use **similes** and **metaphors** to make descriptions in their writing come alive. Similes and metaphors make comparisons between two things that may not have much in common...except for one important characteristic:

   Similes use the word "like" or "as" to make the connection in the comparison.

   > He was as unpredictable as a worn out jack in the box.
   > She shrieked like a howler monkey.

   Metaphors compare by stating that something IS something else.

   > Rodney was a moving train wreck, dropping books and writing utensils all the way to his desk.
   > His desk was a toxic waste site—I sometimes held my breath when I walked past.

   Underline the simile in the passage.

   Now write a metaphor to describe how the boy stood. _____

   _____

   _____

Grammar 5: Sheet 7

Call it Courage, p. 58:

> Mafatu had discovered a mulberry tree. He stripped off the bark and removed the inner white lining. Then he wet the fiber and laid it upon a flat stone and set about beating it with a stick of wood. The fiber spread and grew thinner under the persistent beating. Soon he had a yard of "cloth" to serve as a *pareu.* It was soft and white, and now at last he was clothed.

F.Y.I.: Adjectives

　　Is your bed *soft*? Do you have *long* legs? Will you wear *blue* jeans tomorrow? The words *soft, long* and *blue* are all **adjectives**—words that describe or modify nouns. They add to our understanding of nouns. If we told you about Duane's *greasy, slimy, smelly* lunch box, you would have a very different picture in your mind than when we told you about Robert's *shiny, squeaky clean* lunch box.

Exercises

1. Draw arrows from the adjectives in the passage to the nouns they modify. Do not include articles.

2. **Synonyms** are two words that have the same (or nearly the same) meaning:

   　　　　good—great　　bad—awful

   Antonyms are two words or ideas that have opposite meanings:

   　　　　hard—soft　　　　　sharp—dull

   Think of two antonyms each for the following words. Feel free to use prepositional phrases, clauses, or other longer means of expressing the opposite idea!

   inner _____　　　**white** _____

   wet _____　　　**flat** _____

   thinner _____　　　**soft** _____

3. Write the verbs that modify the following subjects:

   Mafatu _____ _____　　**He** _____ and _____

   he _____ _____　　　　**and** _____ _____

   fiber _____ and _____　　**he** _____

4. Write **art** above the articles.

5. Why is **pareu** italicized? (Check one.)

☐ **Because it is a title.**

☐ **Because it is a foreign word.**

☐ **For emphasis.**

☐ **So we can tell that the author is calling attention to it as a word; we ought not to read it as an integral part of the sentence.**

Grammar 5: Sheet 8

Call it Courage, p. 79:

Never again need he hang his head before his people. He had fought the sea for life and won. He had sustained himself by his own wits and skill. He had faced loneliness and danger and death, if not without flinching, at least with courage. He had been, sometimes, deeply afraid, but he had faced fear and faced it down. Surely that could be called courage.

F.Y.I.: Coordinating Conjunctions

Coordinating conjunctions connect words, phrases or clauses of equal importance. Since there are only seven coordinating conjunctions, remember them by memorizing the acronym **FAN BOYS**:

For	But
And	Or
Nor	Yet
	So

Exercises

1. Write **cc** above all the coordinating conjunctions.

2. Write the verbs that modify the following subjects.

    he _____ _____   He _____ _____ and _____

    He _____ _____   He _____ _____

    He _____ _____   he _____ _____ and _____

    that _____ _____ _____

3. Write **n** above the nouns. **Hint**: In this dictation, **flinching** is a noun.

4. Write **pro** above the pronouns. **Hint**: The word **that** in the final sentence is a pronoun.

5. Use slashes to divide into syllables: **people, sustained, himself, loneliness, danger, courage, deeply, afraid, Surely**

6. Write two new verbs for the sentence **He had fought the sea for life and won.** _____

    _____

7. Circle the antecedent of **it** in the next-to-last sentence.

8. Rewrite the second sentence as if Mafatu was speaking. _____

    _____

This page intentionally left blank.

Passage

Red Sand, Blue Sky, p. 18:

Sand and scrub! She'd never seen anything like this before in her life—a vast expanse of desert sand just lying in wait for a stray willy-willy to stir it into life—a sea of sun-burnt red country dotted with spinifex and mulga, stunted bushes and little old wizened trees. In the distance, the land met the brilliance of the blue sky at a stark horizon.

F.Y.I.: Prepositions, Objects of Prepositions and Prepositional Phrases

Over the river and through the woods...

Are you singing yet? This famous line is from the poem "Boy's Thanksgiving" written by Lydia Maria Child. From these few words, what can you tell about the boy's Thanksgiving Day trip? Clearly he lived in a lush, wooded area, and traveled through it to visit his grandfather. **Prepositions** tell you *where, when,* or *how* something takes place. Most prepositions indicate *direction* or *position.* So where did the boy's sleigh go?

Common Prepositions		
in	on	at
around	through	towards
away	from	under
over	up	down
behind	or	for
by		with

> **Over** the river; **through** the woods

The prepositions **of, by, for,** and **with** don't indicate direction. Instead, they describe logical relationships between things.

> He danced **with** me all night.
> I brought cookies **for** you.

Prepositions usually require an object—a noun or a pronoun—to tell you the *cause* of the action or *where* it takes place (or by whom or what it happens). This noun or pronoun is the **object of the preposition** and completes the meaning of the preposition.

> Kristi hit the ball **over** the <u>net</u>.
> Zach's airplane landed **behind** the <u>couch</u>.

The **preposition** and the **object of the preposition** put together is called a **prepositional phrase**.

> (**Across** the <u>street</u>), children played.
> I have a quarter (**in** my <u>pocket</u>).

Keep in mind that prepositions can have more than one object. When they do, these objects are called **compound objects**.

> When the doorbell rang, Patch scrambled (**over** a <u>sweatshirt</u>, a forgotten math <u>book</u>, a guitar <u>case</u> and finally a bean <u>bag</u>) in order to greet whoever had come to pay him a visit.

Exercises

1. Write **prep** above all prepositions, **op** above all objects of prepositions, and draw parentheses around all prepositional phrases.

2. Use at least two prepositional phrases to describe something. You may use two sentences if you like. When you have completed the assignment, circle the prepositional phrases. _____

   _____

   _____

   _____

3. Is **Sand and scrub!** a complete sentence or a fragment?   **Complete sentence**   **Fragment**

   Why?

   ☐ **It communicates a complete thought**

   ☐ **It lacks a subject.**

   ☐ **It lacks a predicate.**

   ☐ **It includes both subject and predicate**

   ☐ **It is a dependent clause.**

4. **Sand and scrub!** ends with an exclamation point which means it is (an):

   Interjection   **Interrogative**   **Exclamatory**   **Imperative**

5. Write **s** above the subject and **v** above the verb of the last sentence.

6. Overall, what type of paragraph is this? _____

Grammar 5: Sheet 10

Passage

Red Sand, Blue Sky, p. 23:

This mountain range was so different from those she'd seen before in the country north of Melbourne. This was old and worn; worn down by millions of years of wind and rain. Amy suddenly understood what people meant when they said Australia was an old land and for a moment felt small and insignificant next to these ancient red giants.

F.Y.I.: Linking and Helping Verbs

Linking verbs link the subject of the sentence to the predicate noun or adjectives. They describe the way things *are* or *seem* to be.

> The kids *are* sweaty.
> He *seems* happy.

The linked nouns or adjectives are called **predicate nouns** or **predicate adjectives**.

> Sue *is* a **nurse**. (predicate noun)
> That *seems* **backward**. (predicate adjective)

Helping verbs are always used *with* another verb. They control verb tenses and help to express a sense of necessity, certainty, probability or possibility.

> Victor *might* **go** tomorrow
> Katie *will* **leave** soon.

Helping / Linking Verbs				
am	is	are	was	were
have		do		can
has		does		shall
had		did		will
be		may		should
being		might		would
been		must		could

Exercises

1. Write **lv** above the linking verb in the first sentence. Then write **pa** over the predicate adjective.

2. Write **hv** above the helping verb in the first sentence.

3. Write **prep** above all prepositions, **op** above all objects of prepositions, and draw parentheses around all prepositional phrases.

4. Put slashes between the syllables of: **mountain, different, before, country, millions, understood, people, insignificant**

5. Draw an arrow from **they** in the last sentence to its antecedent.

6. Rewrite the last sentence as two shorter sentences. _____

_____

_____

This page intentionally left blank.

Passage   Voice

Red Sand, Blue Sky, p. 44:

They were standing on a little rocky beach and in front of her a sheer rock face rose majestically to meet the sky. A waterhole had been eroded out of the red rock at the foot of the cliff and lay shadowed from the late afternoon sun. The water looked so inviting—cool and still, a mirror of dark green.

F.Y.I.: Voice

We use the term **voice** to describe whether the subject of a sentence is performing the action of the sentence, or if it is being acted upon. An **active-voice** sentence will tell you *who* did the action.

> s   v   do
> The *waitress* served our dessert.

In **passive-voice** sentences, the subject of the sentence is acted upon, but does not perform the action.

> s   hv   v
> The dessert was brought.

There are two key indicators of passive sentences. First, as in our example above, if a sentence doesn't tell you *who* is doing the action, it is written in passive voice.

Secondly, watch for *-ing* endings. When a verb ends in *-ing*, it becomes a noun or adjective. If it is used as a noun, it is called a *gerund*. If it is used as an adjective, it is called a *participle*. If you use gerunds and participles when you write, your sentences are not as strong as if you used true verbs, so try to avoid gerunds and participles when you can.

In order to make passive sentences active, you need to:

1. provide information about who or what performs the action.
2. make sure the subject is the one that acts.

Let's look at another example of a passive sentence.

> s   hv   v   prep op
> The project was completed by *Simon*.

Even though we now know *who* completed the project, this example is still passive: the **project** is still the object of the verb and does not perform the action.

> *Simon* completed the project.   👍

Remember, your written work will be more powerful if you use a lot of active-voice sentences. While it isn't necessary to *always* avoid the passive-voice, keep in mind that it quickly becomes dull and weak. When subjects never act, your writing drags and quickly loses its punch.

Exercises

1. **Adverbs** modify our understanding of verbs. Often (but not always!), adverbs end in –ly. Adverbs can also modify or describe an <u>adjective</u> or another *adverb*.

> Tim arrived in a *ridiculously* <u>hideous</u> sweater.
> Mike drove *unbelievably safely*.

Write the adverbs that modify the following verbs or adjectives:

rose _____   **eroded** _____

afternoon _____

2. Write the adjectives that modify the following nouns:

    beach _____ _____   **face** _____ _____

    rock _____   **sun** _____

    water _____   **green** _____

3. Analyze the first clause: **They were standing....** Label each word using one of the following abbreviations.

    a. Identify the subject (**s**) and verb (**v**).

    b. Label the helping verb (**hv**).

    c. Write **art** above the article.

    d. Write **prep** above the preposition and **op** above the object of preposition.

    e. Label the adjectives (**adj**).

4. **A waterhole had been eroded out of the red rock at the foot of the cliff** is written in the passive voice. Please rewrite it in the active voice. _____

    _____

    _____

5. Write **cc** above all the coordinating conjunctions.

6. Underline the metaphor.

    Write your own metaphor for something with which you are familiar. Use the metaphor from this passage as a model.

    _____

    _____

    _____

    _____

> **N**ot all passive voice is bad! Here are two examples of skillful use of the passive-voice.
>
> For those who have given much, much is required.
> —*John F. Kennedy*
>
> Never in the field of human conflict was so much owed by so many to so few.   —*Winston Churchill*

Grammar 5: Sheet 12

Passage

Red Sand, Blue Sky, p. 53:

But now, for the first time, she realised that there had been a darker side—those who came with guns and hate in their hearts; those who set out to conquer and dominate by whatever means it took; those prepared to kill.

Exercises

1. Circle the dash. Why is it there?

   ☐ **To set off a parenthetical or explanatory remark**

   ☐ **To indicate interrupted speech**

   ☐ **To emphasize the words that follow**

   ☐ **It doesn't belong there**

2. Write the adverbs that modify the following verbs or adjectives:

   realized _____ **set** _____

3. Write **prep** above all prepositions, **op** above all objects of prepositions, and draw parentheses around all prepositional phrases.

4. Place boxes around the semicolons. What are they there for?

   ☐ **To help join two independent clauses in one sentence**

   ☐ **To separate groups that contain commas**

   ☐ **To serve the kind of function that a period does when commas would do**

   ☐ **To provide more substantial breaks than commas would**

   ☐ **They shouldn't be there; the author should have used _____ instead**

5. Analyze the clause **those who came with guns and hate in their hearts**. Use the following list of abbreviations to help you.

   a. Identify the subject (**s**) and verb (**v**).

   b. Write **cc** above the coordinating conjunction.

   c. You should have already labeled the prepositional phrases, so please simply underline the two that belong to this particular clause.

   d. Hint: "those" and "their" help to describe either the subject or the subject's "hearts"—both of which are nouns. Should you label these words **adj** or **adv**?

This page intentionally left blank.

Grammar 5: Sheet 13

Red Sand, Blue Sky, p. 131:

"Careful with that oxygen line," cautioned Barbara.

"Right." Jack braced his back and lifted Caroline's limp form.

"Now keep this flashlight steady on the ground in front of me, Lana," Jack

ordered. "I don't want to trip on these rocks."

F.Y.I.: Clauses, Subordinating Conjunctions

As you already know, a **clause** is a group of related words that include a subject and a predicate. Did you know, however, that there are two main types of clauses? **Independent clauses** contain a *subject* and a predicate, convey a complete thought, and therefore could stand alone as a sentence.

I ran to the store.
She made brownies.

Dependent (or **subordinate**) **clauses** also contain both a subject and a predicate, but they do not convey a complete thought, and therefore could not stand alone as a sentence. They "depend" on another clause to form a complete sentence. Subordinate clauses begin with *subordinating conjunctions*.

Common Subordinating Conjunctions			
after	although	as if	as long as
as though	because	before	in order that
provided that	since	so that	still
that	though	unless	until
when	where	where as	while

Although **I** was tired   ☞   *Although* I was tired, I ran to the store.

when **she** awoke   ☞   She made brownies *when* she awoke.

See the chart for a list of common **subordinating conjunctions**.

Exercises

1. Label the clauses below as either Independent (**ind**) or dependent (**dep**).

   Jack braced his back _____   **[He] lifted Caroline** _____

   After we get there _____   **I don't want to trip** _____

   Since you're standing there _____   **Because Jake was the fastest around** _____

2. Underline the imperative statements.

3. What makes a sentence imperative? _____

   _____

   _____

➡

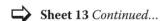

4. Put brackets around all of the prepositional phrases. Write **prep** above the prepositions and **op** above the objects of prepositions.

5. A **direct object** is a noun that *receives* the action or is *affected* by the action from a subject. In the clause "Kyle crashed his car," *car* is the direct object because it is the noun that crashed. When "Anna scrunched her nose," the direct object is *nose* because it is the noun that Anna scrunched. Underline the direct object in the sentences below.

   a. Simon dropped the book.

   b. The cat batted the string.

   c. His hand caught the ball.

6. Analyze the sentence **Jack braced....** Use the following list of abbreviations to help you.

   a. Identify the subject (**s**) and verbs (**v**).

   b. Write **cc** above the coordinating conjunction.

   c. Use **do** to label the direct objects. Hint: there are two.

   d. Label the adjectives (**adj**) that describe the direct objects.

7. Write the subject for the first sentence: _____

Passage

The Big Wave, p. 17:

"And if we are not able?" Kino asked.

"We must be able," his father replied. "Fear alone makes man weak. If you are afraid, your hands tremble, your feet falter, and your brain cannot tell hands and feet what to do."

F.Y.I.: More About Subjects

All clauses contain a subject and a verb, but can you have more than one subject in a clause? Of course! Let's discuss the three varieties of subjects.

Most subjects we've used thus far have been **simple subjects**, which are simply a noun or pronoun by itself.

> **Jeff** wrote on the wall.

Compound subjects include two or more simple subjects.

> **Jeff** and **Duane** wrote on the wall.

A **complete subject** includes both a simple or compound subject, and any words (including adjectives, adverbs or articles) that modify or describe the subject.

> **Those boys** wrote on the wall.
> **The tall, brave, and slightly crazy young man** wrote on the wall.

Exercises

1. Identify the boldface subjects below as either **simple**, **compound** or **complete**.

Kevin ran.	Simple	Compound	Complete
Jorge and **Ben** dashed across the street.	Simple	Compound	Complete
Ainsley, **Zach** and stinky **Pete** hurried to the park.	Simple	Compound	Complete
Ainsley, **Zach** and **stinky Pete** hurried to the park.	Simple	Compound	Complete
Those **paintings** look ridiculous.	Simple	Compound	Complete
Those garish paintings look ridiculous.	Simple	Compound	Complete

2. Write **lv** above the linking verbs in the passage, and…

   Write **pn** or **pa** above any predicate nouns or predicate adjectives.

3. Write **hv** above the helping verbs.

4. Write **s** above the subjects of the passage, **v** above the action verbs.

5. Write the adjectives that modify the following nouns from the passage.

   father _____   **hands** _____

   feet _____   **brain** _____

6. Write three new adjectives for each of the following nouns:

   father _____

   hands _____

   feet _____

   brain _____

   fear _____

7. Add pronouns where you think one or two are missing in the final sentence.

8. Circle the homophones of **wee, knot, bee, week, yew, yore, feat, two,** and **due**.

Grammar 5: Sheet 15

Passage   **Appositives**

The Big Wave, p. 32:

To die a little later or a little sooner does not matter. But to live bravely, to

love life, to see how beautiful the trees are and the mountains, yes, and even the

sea, to enjoy work because it produces food for life—in these things we Japanese

are a fortunate people. We love life because we understand that life and death

are necessary to each other.

F.Y.I.: Appositives

Appositives clarify nouns and appear immediately after them. They are usually set off by one or two commas, and either rename or describe the noun (or pronoun). For example:

Bubba, *the bravest of them all*, was welcomed as a hero.

From this sentence, we now know two things about Bubba: that he was brave and that he was welcomed as a hero. Appositives can also appear at the beginning of a sentence…

A speedy typist, Bo could code a web page in a New York minute.

Or at the end…

I stared at Sophie, *the craziest cat I know*.

Or may not have a comma at all:

We *girls* whispered and giggled until Grandma finally hollered up the stairs.

Exercises

1. Write **appos** above the appositive that comes after the dash in the second sentence.

   Did the author punctuate the appositive correctly?

   ☐ **Yes, she set it off with commas**

   ☐ **No, she did not set it off with commas**

   ☐ **Yes, she attached it directly to the noun it modifies**

   ☐ **No, she did not attach it directly to the noun it modifies**

2. Use an appositive to combine these two sentences into one.

   Cherie was an attractive girl.   Cherie loved to stand with the wind in her hair and her toes in the sand.

Grammar 5 ◆ Activity Sheets ◆ Sheet 15

©2010 by Sonlight Curriculum, Ltd. All rights reserved.

⇨ **Sheet 15** *Continued...*

3. The author uses many infinitives. Write **inf** above each of the infinitives.

4. Why is **to each other** not an infinitive?
    - ☐ **But it is an infinitive!**
    - ☐ **Because it is a prepositional phrase**
    - ☐ **Because it is a partial plural**
    - ☐ **Because it is a clause**

5. Put boxes around any compound words, then use slashes to divide them into their parts.

6. Analyze the clause **in these things...fortunate people** using following symbols: **s**, **lv**, **pn**, **prep**, **op**, **adj**, and **art**.
    If you find a prepositional phrase, please surround it with parentheses. **Note:** you should have already marked the appositive (**appos**).

Passage

Born in the Year of Courage, p. 51:

Later they were bidden back to the table, and this time the servers brought bowls of rice. Manjiro's eyes filled with tears. The wise man had been wrong. These people were not barbarians; they were kind—and they ate rice.

F.Y.I.: Sentence Structures

Independent and dependent clauses build **sentences**—sentences which come in four basic structures.

Simple sentences are an independent clause by itself.

> Pam loved green beans.

Compound sentences are two simple sentences joined together by:

A *coordinating conjunction*:
> Pam loved green beans *and* she ate them every day.

A *coordinating conjunction* and a *comma*:
> Pam loved green beans, *but* I couldn't stand the smell of them.

A *semicolon*:
> Pam loved green beans; Amber brought her a can of them every day.

Complex sentences consist of an [independent] and a (dependent) clause.

> (Although they made her lunch sack heavy), [Pam loved green beans].

Compound-complex sentences contain two [independent clauses] and one (dependent clause).

> (As long as I'm not interrupted), [I can finish the book tonight],
>   [but I will need to work on the paper tomorrow].

Exercises

1. Evaluate each sentence in the passage. Then circle the correct structure for each.

First:	**Simple**	**Compound**	**Complex**	**Compound-Complex**
Second:	**Simple**	**Compound**	**Complex**	**Compound-Complex**
Third:	**Simple**	**Compound**	**Complex**	**Compound-Complex**
Fourth:	**Simple**	**Compound**	**Complex**	**Compound-Complex**

2. Circle the semicolon. Why is it there?

   ☐ **To help join two independent clauses in one sentence**

   ☐ **To separate groups that contain commas**

   ☐ **To serve the kind of function that a period does when a comma would do**

   ☐ **To provide a more substantial break than a comma would**

   ☐ **It shouldn't be there; the author should have used _____ instead**

3. Write **s** above the simple subject of the second sentence. Underline the complete subject of the second sentence.

4. Draw a squiggly line under the simple predicate of the second sentence.
    Double underline the complete predicate of the third sentence.

5. Write **prep** above all prepositions, **op** above all objects of prepositions, and draw parentheses around all prepositional phrases.

6. The author wrote the first clause of the first sentence in the passive voice. Rewrite that clause in the active voice.

    _____

    _____

    _____

7. Analyze the last sentence. Use the following symbols: **s**, **v**, **lv**, **pa**, **pn**, **adj**, **adv**, **cc**, **do**.

Grammar 5: Sheet 17

Passage

Born in the Year of Courage, p. 89:

Manjiro nodded, although he knew he was right. The time in the womb counted as the first year. All babies turned two with the coming of the new year after their birth. He was sixteen.

F.Y.I.: Gerunds

A **gerund** is a noun that has been made from a verb by adding the *-ing* ending. For example:

ski ☞ I love *skiing*.

Note: In general, if you use gerunds when you write, you are using passive voice! Try to avoid gerunds whenever possible: I love *to ski*.

Exercises

1. Rewrite the third sentence to eliminate the gerund **coming**. _____

   _____

   _____

2. Write **pro** above the final pronoun and draw an arrow to its antecedent.

3. Put slashes between the syllables of: **nodded, counted, babies, turned, after, sixteen.**

4. Draw brackets around each clause in today's assignment.

5. Evaluate each sentence in the passage and circle the correct structure for each:

First:	**Simple**	**Compound**	**Complex**	**Compound-Complex**
Second:	**Simple**	**Compound**	**Complex**	**Compound-Complex**
Third:	**Simple**	**Compound**	**Complex**	**Compound-Complex**
Fourth:	**Simple**	**Compound**	**Complex**	**Compound-Complex**

6. What type of sentence is the last one?

   Imperative   **Interrogative**   **Exclamatory**   **Declarative**

7. Analyze the first sentence. Use the following symbols: **pa, sc, s, v. Hint:** you may find a review of subordinating conjunctions helpful.

8. What is the youngest Manjiro could have been? (Suppose he had been born the day before the Japanese New Year.)

   _____

   _____

This page intentionally left blank.

Grammar 5: Sheet 18

Born in the Year of Courage, p. 121:

Manjiro nodded. "Captain Whitfield told me about your friend who escaped from Japan—then took his life. I expect he believed he had dishonored his family."

"Including his ancestors," Dr. Judd said. "And he felt that he had offended the soul of Japan." He shrugged. "I didn't understand then, and I don't now. Nor do I understand Japan's isolationist attitude."

F.Y.I.: Person and Number

Which pronoun should you use if you'd like to talk about yourself? (I). Which pronoun should you use if you'd like to tell your mom that you and your best friend are headed to the park? (We). What if you'd like to point out that the dog is the one responsible for the mess in the living room? (He or she). In English, the pronouns we use are defined by both **person** (first, second and third), and **number** (singular or plural). The first table shows the pronouns we usually use to express each form.

Note: in English, we do not have a separate pronoun for second person plural. In formal English, we may say "you" or "you all," though conversational English might use "you guys," or in some regions "y'all".

Sometimes verb forms are affected by person and number. Let's look at the verb "to be" in the second table.

	Number:	
Person:	Singular	Plural
First Person	I	we
Second Person	you	you (plural)
Third Person	he / she / it	they

Table 1

For these verbs that change, be careful that the subjects in sentences you write "agree" with the verbs. Sentences such as "**I** *are* hungry." and "**Frank** and **Beans** *is* going, too." probably sound funny because they contain agreement errors. If you are careful to keep both pronoun-antecedent pairs and subject-verb pairs aligned to the same person and number, you will avoid many agreement errors.

	Singular	Plural
First Person	I *am*	we *are*
Second Person	you *are*	you (plural) *are*
Third Person	he / she / it *is*	they *are*

Table 2

Exercises

1. Write the person (first, second, third) and number (singular, plural) of the following:

   me _____ _____   your _____ _____

   his _____ _____   I _____ _____

2. Write a pronoun used to express the following person and number.

   first-person, plural: _____   **third-person, singular, masculine:** _____

   second person, singular: _____   **third-person, plural:** _____

   ⇨

3. Write an antonym for:

    life _____   **friend** _____

    escaped _____   **offended** _____

    soul _____   **understand** _____

4. Underline the sentence fragment.

    Rewrite it as a complete sentence. _____

    _____

5. Write **n** above each of the nouns and place check marks above the proper nouns.

6. Analyze the sentences **He shrugged** and **I didn't understand...now**. You will use the following symbols: **adv, cc, do, hv, s, v**. Please consider the contractions as two separate words.

Grammar 5: Sheet 19

Passage

Born in the Year of Courage, p. 146:

"Ye're a thief!" the big man yelled. "An egg-sucking, lily-livered…"

Like a bullet, the older man's left fist slammed upward into the Irishman's

stomach, and as the Irishman bent over, the older man clipped his neck with the

side of his palm.

Exercises

1. Circle the ellipsis.

2. Why did the author use an ellipsis in this passage?

   ☐ **To show a pause**   ☐ **To show that words were left out**

   ☐ **So she didn't have to use a comma**   ☐ **To introduce a series**

3. Match each hyphenated example to the correct explanation of the hyphen's use.

   _____ **to join two or more words in compound numbers**   a. life-long friend

   _____ **to join single letters to other words**   b. 42-0

   _____ **to make compound words**   c. a man-eating shark vs. a man eating shark

   _____ **to join numbers in scores, time spans, etc.**   d. thirty-one

   _____ **to join two or more words that form an adjective before a noun**   e. time-sensitive

   _____ **to prevent confusion**   f. T-shirt

4. Underline the words that are hyphenated.

5. Why did the author use hyphens in this passage?

   ☐ **To divide a word on separate lines**   ☐ **To prevent confusion**

   ☐ **To create new adjectives**   ☐ **To form numbers from twenty-one to ninety-nine**

6. Put a squiggly line under the simile. Then write a sentence using a simile of your own here: _____

   _____

7. Analyze the clause **the older man clipped…palm**. You will use the following symbols: **adj**, **art**, **do**, **prep**, **op**, **s**, **v**. If you find a prepositional phrase, please surround it with parentheses.

This page intentionally left blank.

Grammar 5: Sheet 20

Passage

The Cat Who Went to Heaven, p. 16:

"Run! run!" he exclaimed. "Buy tea and cakes" and he pressed into the old woman's hands the last thing of value he owned, the vase that stood in the alcove of his room and always held a branch or spray of flowers. But even if his room must be bare after this, the artist did not hesitate: No guest could be turned away without proper entertainment.

Exercises

1. What is the meaning of the colon in the last sentence?

   ☐ **What came before is separate from what comes after.**

   ☐ **What follows is a quotation.**

   ☐ **What follows is important.**

   ☐ **What follows is a subtitle.**

   ☐ **What follows explains or expands upon what came before.**

2. There are three errors in the following segment. Please rewrite it to correct the errors.
   "Run! run!" he exclaimed. "Buy tea and cakes" and he pressed into the old woman's hands the last thing of value he owned. Hint: The entire segment may read better if you move the attribution. _____

   _____

   _____

   _____

3. Is **Run!** a complete sentence, or just a fragment?   **A complete sentence**   **Just a fragment**
   Why? _____

   _____

4. Supposing it is a complete sentence: what type of sentence is the quotation in the first sentence?
   (Circle all that apply.)

       Imperative   **Interrogative**   **Exclamatory**   **Declarative**

5. Write **prep** above all prepositions, **op** above all objects of prepositions, and draw parentheses around all prepositional phrases.

⇨

⇨ **Sheet 20** *Continued...*

6. **Challenge:** Put square brackets around the appositive and draw an arrow that points to the noun it modifies.

7. Analyze the last sentence. You will use the following symbols: **adj, adv, art, cc, hv, lv, pa, prep, op, sc, s, v.**

Grammar 5: Sheet 21

The Cat Who Went to Heaven, p. 32:

"But where is the cat?" thought the artist to himself, for even in his vision he remembered that in none of the paintings he had ever seen of the death of Buddha, was a cat represented among the other animals.

"Ah, the cat refused homage to Buddha," he remembered, "and so by her own independent act, only the cat has the doors of Paradise closed in her face."

F.Y.I.: Roots, Prefixes and Suffixes

   All words have a **root**, or a core meaning. For example, you know that the words skis, skiing, ski jumps, and waterskiing all have to do with gliding across a surface with some sort of long planks attached to your feet. We can add parts to root words to change the meaning:

Prefixes appear before the root...

     do ☞ <u>un</u>do.

Suffixes appear after the root...

     do ☞ do<u>ing</u>.

Some words have both a prefix and a suffix:

    <u>un</u>believ<u>eable</u> <u>pre</u>school<u>er</u>

*un*imagin<u>able</u>

*re*place<u>ment</u>

*pre*maturel<u>y</u>

Exercises

1. Draw slashes to divide the root from the prefix in each of the following.

  abnormal   **impossible**   **disadvantage**   **unplug**

  Draw slashes to divide the root from the suffix in each of the following.

  paintings   **bravely**   **watchful**   **sooner**

2. Underline two words that have both a prefix and a suffix. Write each part of the words here.

  _____ _____ ‖ _____ _____ _____

3. Write synonyms for the following:

  cat _____   **artist** _____

  vision _____   **death** _____

  homage _____   **independent** _____

⇨

4. Circle the homophones of **butt**, **wear**, **nun**, and **scene**.

5. Write **n** above each common noun and place a check mark above each of the proper nouns.

6. Write **prep** above all prepositions, **op** above all objects of prepositions, and draw parentheses around all prepositional phrases.

7. Analyze the last sentence through the word **act**. You will use the following symbols: **adj**, **art**, **cc**, **do**, **int**, **prep**, **op**, **sc**, **s**, **v**. Hint: **Ah** is an interjection.

8. **Challenge:** Divide the first paragraph into two or more shorter sentences. _____

_____

_____

_____

_____

Grammar 5: Sheet 22

Passage

Sadako & The Thousand Paper Cranes, pp. 34–36:

"Don't you remember that old story about the crane?" Chizuko asked. "It's supposed to live for a thousand years. If a sick person folds one thousand paper cranes, the gods will grant her wish and make her healthy again." She handed the crane to Sadako. "Here's your first one."

Exercises

1. Please copy the contractions from the passage in the spaces below, then write the original words for which they stand.

    _____ : _____

    _____ : _____

    _____ : _____

2. Rewrite the first sentence so that it no longer contains a contraction ("un-contract" the contraction).

    _____

    _____

    Now, rewrite the first sentence to eliminate the negative adverb. _____

    _____

    _____

3. **Homographs** are words that are spelled the same but have different meanings. Keep in mind, however, that homographs may or may not sound the same. For example:

    > *dove*—type of bird
    > *dove*—to plunge headfirst into water

    The word **crane** is a homograph. Think of one additional meaning of the word.

    crane _____*bird*_____   **crane** _____

4. Write **sc** above the subordinating conjunction.

5. What sentence structure does the third sentence **If a sick person...** have?

    For a refresher on sentence structures, see Sheet 16.

Simple	Compound	Complex	Compound-Complex

⇨

6. Draw a squiggly underline under the independent clause of the third sentence. Does it have a simple or compound predicate?   **Simple**   **Compound**

7. Underline the complete predicate of the next-to-last sentence.

8. The first quoted sentence is what? (Circle all appropriate answers.)

   Imperative   **Interrogative**   **Exclamatory**   **Declarative**

9. Analyze the first sentence. You will use the following symbols: **adj, adv, art, do, hv, prep, op, s, v**. If you find a prepositional phrase, please surround it with parentheses.

Passage

The Kite Fighters, p. 32:

"Well earned, flier," he said, and bowed.

Young-sup bowed in return. He exchanged the kite he had been using for the reel, and for a brief moment the eyes of the man and the boy met. The look they exchanged spoke of their love of flying; no more words were needed.

F.Y.I.: Nouns of Direct Address

"Did you feed the wombats, *Robert*?"

"*Shirley*, I fed them an hour ago." Robert responded. "You did remember, *Elton*, to clean out the cage?"

In the dialog above, can you tell to whom Robert directed his responses? Yes! Since Robert so carefully named each person as he spoke, we can easily see that he was speaking to more than one person.

A **noun of direct address** does just that—it identifies to whom one is speaking. Always use commas to separate nouns of direct address from the rest of the sentence.

"Have you decided what you'll do with your bonus, *Kurt*?"

"Seriously, *Bo*, the website looks phenominal!"

"*Lance*, why is everything broken?"

Exercises

1. Why is there a comma before the word **flier** in the first sentence?

   ☐ **Because whenever you write a word of admiration, you should always set it off with commas.**

   ☐ **Because when you write a noun of direct address, you should always set it off with commas.**

   ☐ **Because you should always use commas to set off introductory clauses.**

   ☐ **Because it sounds right.**

2. The author wrote the final clause **no more words were needed** in the passive voice. Rewrite it in the active voice.

   _____

   _____

3. Two words contain both prefixes and suffixes. They are actually the same word. Underline them.

4. Circle the semicolon. Circle the correct reason why it is in the sentence.

   ☐ **To help join two independent clauses in one sentence**

   ☐ **To separate groups that contain commas**

   ☐ **To provide a more substantial break than a comma would**

   ☐ **It shouldn't be there; the author should have used _____ instead**

➪

5. Analyze the first half of the third sentence (up to the comma). You will use the following symbols: **art, do, hv, prep, op, s, v**. If you find a prepositional phrase, please surround it with parentheses.

Grammar 5: Sheet 24

God's Adventurer: Hudson Taylor, p. 31 (paraphrased):

Tears welled slowly up in the older man's eyes as he looked at the strangely radiant expression of the open-faced boy before him, and he said in a voice deepened by emotion:

"I'd give all the world for a faith like yours."

"You can have it, you know, sir," answered Hudson quietly. "It's free to all—without money and without price."

F.Y.I.: Parenthetical Expressions

A **parenthetical expression** is a remark inserted into another thought, but does not directly deal with the topic at hand. Shorter parentheticals are set off by commas, but longer expressions may be set off by dashes or parentheses. For example:

> My dad—*your grandpa*—is a very funny man.
> *Of course,* that will only start to stink if you open it.
> Yesterday, I ran a mile *(even though I prefer to swim)* and finished 100 crunches.

Exercises

1. Circle the one parenthetical expression.

2. Write **nda** above a noun of direct address.

3. Write the adjectives that modify the following nouns:

   eyes _____   **expression** _____

   boy _____

4. Two adverbs—**slowly** and **up**—modify the verb **welled** in the first sentence. Please rearrange the words in the clause **Tears welled slowly up** in three different ways. Place a check mark by the version you like best.

   _____

   _____

   _____

5. Write **prep** above all prepositions, **op** above all objects of prepositions, and draw parentheses around all prepositional phrases.

6. Analyze the last paragraph. You will use the following symbols: **adv, cc, do, lv, hv, nda, pa, prep, op, s, v.**

This page intentionally left blank.

Passage **Infinitives**

God's Adventurer: Hudson Taylor, p. 50:

Hudson had been in his cabin praying for only a short while, when he felt so certain that God was going to send a breeze that he got up from his knees, went on deck, and suggested to the first officer that he let down the corners of the mainsail.

"What would be the good of that?" asked the first officer scornfully.

"We have been asking God to send a wind, and it's coming immediately!" explained Hudson.

F.Y.I.: Infinitives

Infinitives are a *verbal* formed from the word "to" plus the simplest form of a verb. "To run," "to jump," and "to dance" are all infinitives.

Infinitives function as a noun, adjective or adverb within sentences. Since an infinitive is based on a verb it expresses action or state of being the way verbs do. Here are examples of infinitives…

…as a **subject**:	*To leave* seemed silly since we'd only just arrived.
…as an **adjective**:	Martha knew the best time *to start*.
…as an **adverb**:	We scampered to the tree *to win*.

Note: Be careful not to confuse infinitives with prepositional phrases that begin with the word **to**. In the above example, **to the tree** is a prepositional phrase, and **to win** modifies the verb **scampered**. Just remember that infinitives are always **to** plus a *verb*. Try inserting the words **in order** to test if you've discovered an adverbial infinitive. If the **in order** seems to fit, the infinitive is adverbial.

We scampered to the tree in order to win.

Exercises

1. Write **inf** above the infinitives.

2. People often confuse the words **it's** and **its**. The word **it's** is the contraction of **it is**. The word **its** is a possessive pronoun. Which of these two words do you find in this passage? Circle it and circle its correct definition:

   Contraction   **Possessive**

3. Draw an arrow from the final pronoun to its antecedent.

4. Why does this passage have three paragraphs?

    ☐ **Because, when you're writing dialog, whenever the actor or speaker changes, you should start a new paragraph.**

    ☐ **There is no good reason; the author made a mistake.**

5. What is the structure of the last quotation?

    Simple   **Compound**   **Complex**   **Compound-Complex**

6. Analyze the second sentence. You will use the following symbols: **adj, adv, art, hv, lv, pa, prep, op, s, v.**

Grammar 5: Sheet 26

Passage

God's Adventurer: Hudson Taylor, p. 72:

Months ago he had taken the step of dressing exactly as the Chinese did. He had called down a good deal of criticism on himself from fellow-Europeans for it, but he was able to mingle much more freely with the Chinese themselves, and had travelled extensively in places where most Europeans would have been mobbed.

Exercises

1. Draw brackets around each of the clauses in the first sentence. Mark any independent clauses with **ind** and any dependent clauses with **dep**.

   Based on your analysis, what is its sentence structure?

   Simple   **Compound**   **Complex**   **Compound-Complex**

2. Draw brackets around each clause in the second sentence. Mark any independent clauses with **ind** and any dependent clauses with **dep**.

   Based on your analysis, what is its sentence structure?

   Simple   **Compound**   **Complex**   **Compound-Complex**

3. Write **prep** above all prepositions, **op** above all objects of prepositions, and draw parentheses around all prepositional phrases.

4. **Dressing** is a gerund. Please rewrite the first sentence to eliminate the gerund. For extra credit, write the sentence without an infinitive! _____

   _____

   _____

5. The author used the passive voice to write the clause **where most Europeans would have been mobbed**. Please rewrite it in the active voice. _____

   _____

   _____

6. Overall, what type of paragraph is this?   **Expository**   **Persuasive**   **Descriptive**   **Narrative**

7. Analyze the first sentence. You will use the following symbols: **adv, art, do, hv, prep, op, s, sc, v.**

This page intentionally left blank.

Grammar 5: Sheet 27

Passage

God's Adventurer: Hudson Taylor, p. 89:

Mr. Nee rose to his feet. All eyes were turned to him as he said, with quiet, oriental gravity:

"I have long sought the truth, as my father did before me, without finding it. I travelled far and near, searching for the Way, but never found it. In the teachings of Confucius, the doctrines of Buddhism and Taoism, I have found no rest. But I have found rest in what we have heard tonight. From now on I am a believer in Jesus."

F.Y.I.: Verb Tenses

A **verb's tense** tells you when an action occurs—in the *past, present* or *future*. However, since actions can happen once or over a period of time, there are several types of tenses. (Notice that many forms require helping verbs!)

Use *simple* tenses when the action simply happens.

Simple past:	Zachary jump*ed*.
Simple present:	Zachary jump*s*.
Simple future:	Zachary *will* jump.

Use *continuing* tenses when the action continues to happen over a period of time.

Continuing past:	Zachary *was* jump*ing*.
Continuing present:	Zachary *is* jump*ing*.
Continuing future:	Zachary *will be* jump*ing*.

Use *past perfect* tense when the action ends prior to another past action:

Zachary *had* jump*ed*.

Use *present perfect* tense when the action started in the past but continues or is completed in the present:

Zachary *has* jump*ed*.

Use *future perfect* tense to express an action that will begin and be completed by a specific time in the future:

Zachary *will have* jump*ed*.

Exercises

1. What is the tense of the second to last sentence?

    Simple Past   **Present Perfect**   **Future Perfect**

2. What is the sentence structure of **I travelled far and near...but never found it**?

    Simple   **Compound**   **Complex**   **Compound-Complex**

3. Write the person (first, second, third) and number (singular, plural) of the final sentence.

    _____   _____

4. Write synonyms for the following words:

    quiet _____   **sought** _____

    father _____   **travelled** _____

    near _____   **found** _____

5. Write **prep** above all prepositions, **op** above all objects of prepositions, and draw parentheses around all prepositional phrases.

6. Analyze the first sentence of the second paragraph.

    You will use the following symbols: **adj**, **adv**, **art**, **do**, **hv**, **prep**, **op**, **obj**, **s**, **sc**, **v**.

Passage

God's Adventurer: Hudson Taylor, p. 101:

Hudson never doubted that God would answer his prayer. Nor did it trouble him that he, who had barely enough money to support his wife and family, would now begin to require an income of thousands of pounds a year to support the twenty-four willing, skilful laborers. If he was doing God's work in God's way, God would certainly send in the money required!

F.Y.I.: Pronoun Case

Did you know that each personal pronoun has three **cases**? A pronoun's **case** changes form in relation to other words.

1. **Nominative**—when the pronoun is the subject of a sentence.

    I hit the ball.

2. **Possessive**—when the pronoun owns something.

    My ball went over the fence.

3. Use **objective** pronouns when the pronoun is the object of the sentence, so it *receives* or is *affected by* the action from a subject.

    Michael soaked *me* with the hose.

This table shows pronouns according to case, person and number of the noun.

Pronouns				
Person/Number	Nominative/Subject	Possessive		Objective/Object
1st/Singular	**I** went to school.	This is **my** house.	This house of **mine**.	That soaked **me**.
1st/Plural	**We** went to school.	This is **our** house.	This house of **ours**.	That soaked **us**.
2nd/Singular	**You** went to school.	This is **your** house.	This house of **yours**	That soaked **you**.
2nd/Plural	**You** went to school.	This is **your** house.	This house of **yours**.	That soaked **you**.
3rd/Singular Masc	**He** went to school.	This is **his** house.	This house of **his**	That soaked **him**.
3rd/Singular Fem	**She** went to school.	This is **her** house.	This house of **hers**.	That soaked **her**.
3rd/Singular Neut	**It** went to school.	This is **its** house.		That soaked **it**.
3rd/Plural	**They** went to school.	This is **their** house.	This house of **theirs**.	That soaked **them**.

➡

Exercises

1. Write the correct case (nominative, objective, or possessive) beside the following pronouns from the passage:

   his _____   **it** _____

   him _____   **he** _____

   his _____   **he** _____

2. Put a box around the possessive nouns.

3. Write **inf** above the infinitives.

4. Underline the parenthetical expression.

5. Double underline the exclamatory sentence.

6. Draw brackets around each of the clauses in each sentence. Mark any independent clauses with **ind** and any dependent clauses with **dep**.

   Based on your analysis, what is the structure of the…

First sentence?	**Simple**	**Compound**	**Complex**	**Compound-Complex**
Second sentence?	**Simple**	**Compound**	**Complex**	**Compound-Complex**
Third sentence?	**Simple**	**Compound**	**Complex**	**Compound-Complex**

7. Analyze the first sentence. You will use the following symbols: **adj**, **adv**, **do**, **hv**, **s**, **sc**, **v**.

Passage

Li Lun, Lad of Courage, p. 27:

He stood up and shouldered the bundles again, happy that he was toiling up the mountain instead of sailing over the sea. The rocks were at peace among themselves; the waves were not.

F.Y.I: Personification

*The brook skipped along under the trees, giggling and laughing,
inviting us to kick off our shoes and come in for a dip.*

Wait…can a brook really skip, giggle and laugh? No, but the sentence gives you a clear and interesting description of the brook, doesn't it? This sentence is an example of **personification**, which gives an inanimate object human qualities.

My eraser squeaked an angry protest as I changed my answer a third time.
The house popped and sighed as it, too, settled in for the night.

Write your own example of personification on the back of this Activity Sheet.

Exercises

1. Put parentheses around the personification in the passage.

2. Draw slashes between the root words and suffixes of **shouldered, bundles, toiling, sailing, rocks**, and **waves**.

3. Think of two antonyms or contrastive words for each of the following. Feel free to use prepositional phrases, clauses, or other longer means of expressing the opposite or contrastive idea!

   stood up _____   **happy** _____

   mountain _____   **over** _____

   sea _____   **peace** _____

4. Divide the first sentence into two simple sentences.

   _____

   _____

5. Circle the semicolon. Why is it there?

   ☐ **To help join two independent clauses in one sentence**

   ☐ **To separate groups that contain commas**

   ☐ **To serve the kind of function that a period does when a comma would do;
   to provide a more substantial break than a comma would**

   ☐ **It shouldn't be there; the author should have used _____ instead**

⇨

⇨ **Sheet 29** *Continued...*

6. Analyze the first clause of the first sentence. You will use the following symbols: **adv, art, cc, do, s, v**.

My example of personification:

_____

_____

_____

Grammar 5: Sheet 30

Mission to Cathay, pp. 49–50:

There was much talking to be done, and never had Father Ricci felt so humble. All his life, he had had the gift of tongues, and now he stood begging in this strange land where he had so much to do, begging in a tongue so difficult that he must only sound ridiculous to those from whom he had so much to ask.

F.Y.I.: Cleft Sentences & Delayed Subjects

A **cleft sentence** is a complex sentence formed when a declarative sentence is divided into a main and a subordinate clause in order to emphasize part of the sentence. Cleft sentences usually begin with the word *there* or *it*, followed by a form of the verb *to be*.

> *There were* many people who came to see us off.

Can you write the original sentence we used to form our example?

_____

Since the <u>subject</u> comes after the **verb** in cleft sentences, we consider them "**delayed**" **subjects**.

> There **were** many <u>people</u> who came to see us off.

Subjects are also delayed in questions.

> Who **is** that <u>guy</u>?

Exercises

1. The first sentence begins with **There was....** This structure tells us what about the sentence? It has

   A preposition   **A metaphor**   **A passive voice**   **A delayed subject**

2. Draw brackets around each clause in the first sentence. Mark any independent clauses with **ind** and any dependent clauses with **dep**.

3. What is (or are) the antecedent(s) to all the pronouns **he** in the second sentence? _____

   _____

4. Do the words **All his life** in the second sentence form a phrase or a clause?   **Phrase**   **Clause**

   How do you know?

   ☐ It has both a subject and predicate.

   ☐ It lacks a subject.

   ☐ It lacks a predicate.

⇨ F.Y.I.—Original sentence: Many people came to see us off.

⇨ **Sheet 30** *Continued...*

5. The author wrote the first clause in the passive voice. Please rewrite it in the active voice.

   _____

6. **Challenge:** What is the tense of each of the following clauses?

   Never had Ricci felt so humble.   **Simple past**   **Continuing past**   **Past perfect**

   He had had the gift of tongues.   **Simple past**   **Continuing past**   **Past perfect**

   He must sound ridiculous.   **Simple present**   **Continuing present**   **Present perfect**

7. Analyze the first sentence beginning with the coordinating conjunction.

   You will use the following symbols: **adv**, **cc**, **hv**, **pa**, **s**, **v**.

Passage

Mission to Cathay, p. 84:

"Yes, Youngest," he said, "we must give them back. These foreigners are here by my favor, and it is by my favor that they have their land. If I keep their gifts, it may look as if I have let them stay because of the gifts they have brought me. And no man must be able to point his finger and say that the foreigners have bought Wang P'an."

F.Y.I.: Adjective Forms (or Comparatives)

In addition to providing a simple description, **adjectives** can tell you more about a noun by comparing it to something else. To do so, an adjective will come in one of three **forms**.

The **positive form** describes a word without comparing it to anything else. The positive form is also considered the **root** of an adjective.

> Simon is *silly.*

The **comparative form** compares a word to one other thing. Comparative forms often use the *–er* ending, or include the words *more* or *less.*

> Simon is *more silly* than Grant. (or *sillier*)

The **superlative form** compares a word to two or more things. Superlative adjectives often use the ending *–est* or the words *most* or *least.*

> Simon is the *silliest* kid in the room.

Exercises

1. Put a box around the superlative adjective. Write its root and comparative forms.

   _____   _____

2. Write **inf** above the infinitive.

3. Write **nda** above the noun of direct address. Circle the commas that set it off.

4. Underline the compound predicate in the first clause of the last sentence.

5. What are the following pronouns' persons (first, second, third) and numbers (singular, plural)?

   he _____ _____   **we** _____ _____

   me _____ _____   **I** _____ _____

   they _____ _____   **it** _____ _____

6. What are the tenses of the verbs in the third sentence? Use: simple, continuing, or perfect, **and** past, present, or future.

    keep _____   _____

    may look _____   _____

    have let _____   _____

    have brought _____   _____

7. Use the standard symbols (**s**, **v**, **do**, **adv**, etc.) to analyze the first and second sentences.[1] **Hint**: **Yes** is an adverb.

8. Is the first sentence a good topic sentence—that is, does it do a good job of summarizing the content of the paragraph?

    ☐ **Yes**

    ☐ **Another would be better**

    ☐ **There really isn't a good topic sentence in the paragraph**

    Why? (Discuss your answer with your mom or dad.)

---

1. For a complete list of symbols, please find our List of Standard Symbols in Section Three: Resources.

Passage

Mission to Cathay, p. 103:

Matteo Ricci was unperturbed.

"We cannot have these people thinking that we are swayed by their omens and threats. We must go on, Michele, if only to show them that our God is above such things."

F.Y.I.: Participles and Participial Phrases

A **participle** is a verbal that usually ends in *–ing* or *–ed* (and sometimes in *–en*, *–d*, *–t*, or *–n*) that functions as an adjective to modify a noun or a pronoun. A **participial phrase** consists of a participle and its modifier(s), object(s), or complement(s). Participial phrases are set off by commas when:

1. they appear at the beginning of a sentence
2. they interrupt a sentence as a nonessential element
3. they appear at the end of a sentence and are separated from the noun they modify.

For example:

> Duane, *reclining in his chair*, fought the urge to sleep.
> *Laughing merrily*, we filed back into the building.

To avoid confusion, participles and participial phrases must be placed as close to the nouns and pronouns they modify as possible, and the nouns and pronouns must be clearly stated.

> *Chewing on a chair leg*, KD shrieked at the dog.

In the above example, it would appear that my friend KD has some interesting gnawing habits… As written, **KD** is the noun closest to the participial phrase, so it would appear that she's the one **chewing**, when really, the dog is the one who turned the chair leg into a chew toy. This is an example of a **dangling participle**: the participial phrase has been left "dangling" without a clear antecedent. The above example would be more clear if written as:

> KD shrieked at the dog *chewing on a chair leg*.

Exercises

1. Correctly use the participial phrase **gasping for air** in a sentence of your own. _____

   _____

   _____

2. Rewrite the second sentence and replace the participles **thinking** and **swayed** with action verbs.

   _____

   _____ ⇨

3. Write **nda** above the noun of direct address.

4. Put a box around the word that has both a prefix and suffix.

5. Write the person (first, second, third) and number (singular, plural) of the following pronouns:

    we _____   _____   **their** _____   _____

    our _____   _____

6. Evaluate each sentence in the passage. Then circle the correct structure for each:

First:	**Simple**	**Compound**	**Complex**	**Compound-Complex**
Second:	**Simple**	**Compound**	**Complex**	**Compound-Complex**
Third:	**Simple**	**Compound**	**Complex**	**Compound-Complex**

7. Use the standard symbols to analyze the first sentence.

8. Write **inf** above the infinitive.

Grammar 5: Sheet 33

Mission to Cathay, pp. 166–167:

The Chinese youth, helpless in the priest's grip, yelled his abuse and accusations; the priest poured out torrents of furious Italian, and the boy, understanding the Chinese, yelled at him not to speak so to the honored Father. In the shadows of the starlight and the small lamplight, the pale, shocked faces of three old Mandarins looked at them in horror.

F.Y.I.: Capitalization

We're confident you already know some of the rules of **capitalization**. For example, you already know that sentences need to begin with a capital letter, and that proper nouns—like names—should begin with capitals as well.

Have you ever noticed that not every word in a **title** is capitalized...and yet many of them are? Well, how do you know which ones to capitalize? Here is a brief run-down of the rules:

_Do_ capitalize:

- The first and last word
- ...and every word in between except:

Do NOT capitalize:

- articles:
- short prepositions:
- coordinating conjunctions:

My Son the Marine

"Away in a Manger"

Henry and Risby

The following table describes a few more instances where words either should or shouldn't be capitalized.

Capitalization Rules		
Type of Words	For example...	Don't capitalize...
Abbreviations	FBI, MIA	Have you noticed that if a word serves as a **proper noun**, you capitalize it? The *Southwest* is the name of a specific region in the United States, so it serves as a proper noun. If you *run southwest toward the pond*, "southwest" is now a common noun, so you don't capitalize it!
Associations, teams or organizations	Denver Broncos, Americans	
Days, months and holidays	Friday, December, Valentine's Day	
Religions, Races, Nationalities, and languages	Asian, Christian, German	
References to God, the Bible or books in the Bible	the Lord, God's Word, Ephesians	
Letters to indicate shape	U-turn, V-neck	
Sections of the country	Southwest	...words that indicate direction: Drive *north*.
Special events or periods in history	World War II, the Great Depression	

(Table continued on the following page...)

Capitalization Rules		
Type of Words	For example...	Don't capitalize...
Specific geographical references	North America, Saturn	...general geographical references: We went to *the beach*.
Trade Names	Snickers, Toyota Camry	
Words used as part of a name	Uncle Bubba, Dad	...if these words are not used to replace or compliment a proper noun: Is your *dad* downstairs?

Exercises

1. Underline the word **father**. Sometimes this word is a capitalized and sometimes it is not. How do you know when to capitalize it? _____

   _____

2. Put boxes around all the capitalized words that have to do with different cultures or languages Why are all these words capitalized? _____

   _____

   _____

3. Draw brackets around the participial phrase in the first sentence.

4. Draw a squiggly underline under the appositive in the same sentence.

5. Does the word **Chinese**, in the phrase **understanding the Chinese**, refer to the Chinese language or a Chinese person?

   _____

   _____

6. Rewrite the first sentence so that it is at least three sentences. _____

   _____

   _____

7. Analyze the final sentence. You will use the following symbols: **adj**, **art**, **cc**, **prep**, **op**, **s**, **v**. If you find a prepositional phrase, please surround it with parentheses.

Grammar 5: Sheet 34

Passage

Mission to Cathay, p. 198:

"Come," the Jesuit said to him softly. "Is it not the law in any family that the stronger ones shall care for the weak? Now, here in the Family of the Lord of Heaven, is one weaker than you. You would not neglect him?"

The boy shook his head.

"No, my Father, no," he said.

Exercises

1. Write **nda** above the noun of direct address.

2. Underline the complete predicate in the fourth sentence.

3. Put an asterisk above each of the two comparative adjectives.

   Write the superlative forms of both adjectives. _____ _____

4. Write two antonyms or, at least, contrastive expressions for each of the following words. Feel free to use prepositional phrases, clauses, or other longer means of expressing the opposite idea!

   come _____   **softly** _____

   law _____   **weak** _____

   boy _____   **father** _____

5. What type of sentences end in question marks?

   Imperative   **Interrogative**   **Exclamatory**   **Declarative**

6. Overall, what type of paragraph is the first one?

   Expository   **Persuasive**   **Descriptive**   **Narrative**

7. Why are the last two paragraphs separate from each other?

   ☐ **Because, when you're writing dialog, whenever the actor or speaker changes, you should start a new paragraph.**

   ☐ **There is no good reason; the author made a mistake.**

8. Analyze the first sentence plus the sentence **The boy shook his head**.

   You will use the following symbols: **adj, art, adv, do, prep, op, s, v.**

   Name the subject that modifies the verb **Come**. _____

This page intentionally left blank.

Passage

Mission to Cathay, p. 222:

"He has told me," went on Wang P'an, "how you cared even unto death for this homeless stranger, just as you cared for him himself, when he was without his family. I think the same as the dead man said in his sickness; that there must be much good in a religion such as yours, that teaches men to love and care for each other without hope of gain."

F.Y.I.: Transitive Verbs and Indirect Objects

While many verbs simply require one noun or pronoun to perform the action in a clause...

> **Sam** *ran.* —OR— **They** finally *slept.*[1]

...**Transitive verbs** require two nouns:

1. one noun to serve as the subject to do the action

2. another noun to receive the action or to be acted upon—which is the direct object.

Transitive verbs transfer action from one noun to another:

> s   v   do
> **Jake** *held* my **hand.**

If we simply said **Jake held** ...you'd forever wonder *what* it was that he held. The remote control? An ancient clay pot? A bag of candy? The verb **held** is transitive because it requires you to state an object to *be* held. In this case, my **hand** was what was held, so **hand** is the **direct object**.

> **Jeff** *threw* **Trevor** the **football.**

In the example above, **Jeff** is the subject since he is the one who *threw* (transitive verb) the football. And since the *football* is the thing that was thrown, **football** is the **direct object**. But what about **Trevor**?

Indirect objects receive the action of the transitive verb indirectly. They always come *before* the direct object, and answer "to whom" or "for whom" the action of the verb is done—and who receives the direct object. So since **Trevor** is the one *to whom* Jeff threw the football, **Trevor** is the indirect object.

Note: Indirect objects are always a noun or a pronoun that is *not* part of a prepositional phrase.

> s   v   do   s   v   do   prep art   op
> **Ronak** *hit* the **baseball.**   vs.   **Ronak** *hit* the **baseball** (over the fence).

Keep in mind that a sentence must contain a direct object in order to have an indirect object.

Exercises

1. Underline the direct objects in the sentences below and circle the indirect objects.

    Mama read Zachary the story.   We gave the puppy a bone.

    Robert offered Bo a ride.   Grandpa sold Mark the wheelbarrow.

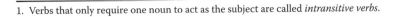

1. Verbs that only require one noun to act as the subject are called *intransitive verbs*.

2. Write the person (first, second, third) and number (singular, plural) of the following pronouns:

    He _____ _____   **me** _____ _____

    you _____ _____   **I** _____ _____

3. Write the correct case (nominative, objective, possessive) beside each pronoun:

    He _____   **me** _____

    you _____   **him** _____

    his _____   **yours** _____

4. Draw a box around the compound words.

5. Analyze the first sentence through the word **stranger**. **Hint: Me** is an indirect object that answers "to whom or for whom the action is done." Technically, the message that was told is the direct object, so in this case, it is an "understood" direct object.

Passage   Adjectival and Adverbial Clauses

Homesick, p. 25:

"Good-bye," I said. "May the River God protect you."

For a moment the boy stared. When he spoke, it was as if he were trying out a new sound. "American friend," he said slowly.

When I looked back, he was still there, looking soberly toward the foreign world to which I had gone.

F.Y.I.: Adjectival and Adverbial Clauses

Remember, a clause is a group of related words that includes a subject and a predicate. You also know that while both independent and dependent clauses contain both subjects and predicates, only independent clauses convey a complete thought and can stand alone as a complete sentence—dependent clauses do not, and cannot.

Did you know that clauses can serve different functions in a sentence? **Adjectival clauses** (also called adjective or relative clauses) usually begin with a *relative pronoun* and serve as an adjective. **Relative pronouns** connect phrases or clauses to nouns or pronouns. The most common relative pronouns are *who, whoever, which* and *that*. For example:

The child *who left her shoes on the stairs* should come and retrieve them.

In the sentence above, **who left her shoes on the stairs** is an adjectival clause because it describes the noun **child**.

Adverbial clauses may begin with a *subordinating conjunction* and serve as an adverb.

I filled the tank with gas *before I went home*.

The clause **before I went home** is an adverbial clause because it describes *when* I filled the tank and begins with the subordinating conjunction **before**.

Exercises

1. **To which I had gone** is an adjectival clause. Draw brackets around the clause and then draw an arrow from the clause to the noun or pronoun it modifies.

2. Draw brackets around each clause in the last sentence. Mark any independent clauses with **ind** and any dependent clauses with **dep.**

    Based on your analysis, what is the structure of this sentence?

    Simple   **Compound**   **Complex**   **Compound-Complex**

3. The word **looking** in the last sentence is a participle. Rewrite the sentence so that you replace the participle with a true verb. _____

_____

4. Write **prep** above all prepositions, **op** above all objects of prepositions, and draw parentheses around all prepositional phrases.

5. The following words are homographs. Think of at least two meanings for each word. We gave you one of them.

   May _____*permission, blessing*_____ _____

   spoke _____*past tense of speak*_____ _____

   back _____*behind*_____ _____

   still _____*yet, continuing*_____ _____

6. Use the standard symbols (**s**, **v**, **do**, **art**, **adj**, etc.) to analyze the second and third sentences.

Passage Topic Sentences

Homesick, p. 61:

Why did I love the river so? It wasn't what you would call beautiful. It wasn't *like* anything. It just *was* and it had always been. When you were on the river or even looking at it, you flowed with time. You were part of forever.

F.Y.I.: Topic Sentences

Do you think it is important to know how to write a good **topic sentence**? Of course it is. A topic sentence introduces the subject of a paragraph and tells the reader what the paragraph is going to discuss. Usually, a topic sentence is the first sentence in a paragraph, though not all paragraphs have a topic sentence. Regardless, they should be used in every persuasive paragraph and in all paragraphs of a formal essay.

My mom makes the best macaroni and cheese.
The craziest thing happened in the park on Friday.

Exercises

1. What is the person of the pronoun:

I	**first**	**second**	**third**
it	**first**	**second**	**third**
you	**first**	**second**	**third**

2. Draw brackets around each clause in the first, second and fourth sentences. Mark any independent clauses with **ind** and any dependent clauses with **dep**.

   Based on your analysis, what is the structure of this sentence?

First:	**Simple**	**Compound**	**Complex**	**Compound-Complex**
Second:	**Simple**	**Compound**	**Complex**	**Compound-Complex**
Fourth:	**Simple**	**Compound**	**Complex**	**Compound-Complex**

3. Write six adjectives that might be used to describe a **river** (or different rivers). Remember that you can use participles and prepositional phrases as adjectives!

   _____   _____

   _____   _____

   _____   _____

4. Put slashes between the syllables of **river**, **beautiful**, **always**, and **flowed**.

5. Put boxes around any compound words, then use slashes to divide them into their parts.

6. Analyze the first and last sentences.

7. Do the words **you flowed with time** in the next-to-last sentence form a phrase or a clause?   **Phrase**   **Clause**

8. Is the first sentence a good topic sentence?

   ☐ **Yes**

   ☐ **Another would be better**

   ☐ **There really isn't a good topic sentence in the paragraph**

   Why? (Discuss your answer with your mom or dad.)

Passage

Homesick, p. 101:

My mother put her arms around Mrs. Hu. My father took one of Mr. Hu's hands in both of his. "Old friend," he said. "Old friend." He must have been misty-eyed, for he took off his glasses and wiped them. Suddenly I found myself blinking back tears and I didn't know why. I was counting the days on the calendar, wasn't I? Then how could a yellow ginger jar turn everything inside me upside down?

F.Y.I : Possessive Nouns & Pronouns

You have stuff. Books, toys, clothes, and maybe a computer or video game here and there, too. If you have any siblings, they have stuff too. Well, when they ask, how do you communicate to mom or dad which one of you owns that toy that was left in the living room? If something belongs to you, you could say you are in *possession* of it. When we write and when we speak, we use **possessive nouns** and **pronouns** to describe what stuff belongs to whom. In a sentence, we can show that nouns possess something by adding an apostrophe-s ('s) or an s-apostrophe (s') to the end of the noun.

Pronouns		
Person/Number	Possessive	
1st/Singular	This is **my** house.	This house of **mine**.
1st/Plural	This is **our** house.	This house of **ours**.
2nd/Singular	This is **your** house.	This house of **yours**
2nd/Plural	This is **your** house.	This house of **yours**.
3rd/Singular Masc	This is **his** house.	This house of **his**
3rd/Singular Fem	This is **her** house.	This house of **hers**.
3rd/Singular Neut	This is **its** house.	
3rd/Plural	This is **their** house.	This house of **theirs**.

Greg owned a calculator   ☞   Greg*'s* calculator.

If more than one person listed in a series owns something, attach the 's to the final noun in the list:

Matt and Pam had children.   ☞   Matt and Pam*'s* children.

If a noun is *plural* and already ends in an *s*, you simply need to add the apostrophe after the *s*.

The kids had toys.   ☞   The kid*s'* toys.

In the example above, more than one kid owned the toys.

Keep in mind that if a noun is singular and ends in an *s* or *z*, you can add either a simple *apostrophe* OR an *'s* to show possession.

Chris*'s* computer   OR   Chris*'* computer

As you discussed with mom or dad earlier this year, pronouns change form to show possession—as shown in the table.

Exercises

1. Place check marks above the possessive nouns and pronouns.

2. Underline the five plural nouns.

3. Circle the past-tense verbs (including helping verbs).

    Rewrite them as present-tense verbs for third person singular pronouns.

    _____   _____

    _____   _____

    _____   _____

    _____   _____

    _____   _____

4. Draw an arrow from the pronoun in the third sentence to its antecedent.

5. A **rhetorical question** is one that is asked without the expectation of an answer because the answer is obvious or simply not required. Double underline any rhetorical questions.

6. Analyze the sentence that begins **He must have been**.

Grammar 5: Sheet 39

Passage

Water Sky, pp. 18–19:

"The whale," Kusiq said quietly, "is our hardware store. We use agviQ—Iñupiat for bowhead whale—for houses, sleds, traps, fishlines, bows, art and even brooms."

"But not anymore," Lincoln said, repeating Uncle Jack's favorite line as he gestured to cardboard boxes and plastic chairs. "You have other materials. You don't need to kill whales anymore."

Exercises

1. Write **n** above the common nouns and place check marks above the proper nouns.

2. Put asterisks above the possessives, both pronoun and noun.

3. Write **prep** above all prepositions, **op** above all objects of prepositions, and draw parentheses around all prepositional phrases. **Note:** In the second paragraph, **as** serves as a coordinating conjunction that means "when" or "while"—it is not a preposition in this context.

4. The series **houses, sleds, traps, fishlines, bows, art and even brooms** could be punctuated differently than it is. Please add and circle the appropriate optional punctuation.

5. Draw arrows that point to the dashes. Why do you think they are there?

   ☐ **To set off a parenthetical or explanatory remark**

   ☐ **To indicate interrupted speech**

   ☐ **To emphasize the words that follow**

   ☐ **They don't belong there**

6. **Repeating** is a participle. Rewrite the sentence and replace the participle with a verb. _____

   _____

7. Draw brackets around and write **appos** above the appositive.

8. Underline the metaphor.

   Discuss with your mom or dad: why do you think this is—or is not—an apt metaphor?

9. Analyze the first sentence.

This page intentionally left blank.

Grammar 5: Sheet 40

Passage

Water Sky, pp. 54–55:

"The air is still," the whaling captain said. "That is good. But the sea current is strong. It is bringing in siku, the pack ice."

"Pack ice?"

"The pack ice is permanent ice. It drifts around the pole all year. It comes and goes. In the spring whaling season it hits the pan ice and smashes it into mountains called pressure ridges."

Exercises

1. Draw brackets around and write **appos** above the appositive.

2. Put parentheses around the prepositional phrases.

3. The following words have suffixes. Circle the root word and underline the suffix in each. If the root has been altered, simply circle the altered remnant: **whaling**, **bringing**, **drifts**, **comes**, **goes**, **hits**, **smashes**, **mountains**, **ridges**.

4. Underline the complete subject of the third sentence.

5. Double underline the sentence fragment.

   Is this acceptable?   **Yes**   **No**

   Why or why not? _____

   _____

6. Analyze the first three sentences.

7. Rewrite the first two sentences of the last paragraph so that they form one sentence. _____

   _____

   _____

   _____

This page intentionally left blank.

Passage **Negative Statements**

Water Sky, p. 112:

The orange-flagged trail snaked around huge ice blocks, across open flats and along the edge of the shore to finally arrive at a radio tower. Vincent signaled, "Stop."

"End of the United States, Point Barrow," said Weir, walking up to Lincoln. The wind-packed snow smoothed the landscape so that Lincoln could not tell where the U.S. ended and the ocean began.

F.Y.I.: Negative Statements

Negative statements express something that is not true, and usually feature words such as *no, not, nothing* and *no one*. For example:

> There is *nothing* left on the plate.
> There are *no* more ornaments to put on the tree.

Keep in mind that *no* and *not* can also be adjectives that modify nouns, adjectives, verbs, or other adverbs.

> I can *not* climb the stairs. (adverb)
> He is *not* a dog. (adjective)

Exercises

1. Underline the negative clause in today's passage.

2. Put an asterisk above the hyphens.

3. Why did the author use hyphens in this passage?

   ☐ **To divide a word on separate lines**   ☐ **To prevent confusion**

   ☐ **To create new adjectives**   ☐ **To separate numbers**

4. Why are some adjectives connected with hyphens and some are not? _____

   _____

   _____

5. Put brackets around all of the prepositional phrases. Write **prep** over the prepositions and **op** over objects of prepositions.

➡️ **Sheet 41** *Continued...*

6. In this passage **ocean** is not capitalized, but sometimes it is. How do you know when to capitalize this word?

   _____

   _____

7. Use the standard symbols to analyze the final sentence.

8. Rewrite the first sentence with a different verb. _____

   _____

   _____

   _____

Passage

Water Sky, p. 169:

Musk Ox held the harpoon where Little Owl had aimed it. Then suddenly he turned, pulled Kusiq to his feet and gave the harpoon to him.

Kusiq took it eagerly, and with a loud grunt threw it. The harpoon hit the mark and disappeared. The whale plunged.

F.Y.I.: Nonrestrictive & Restrictive Phrases and Clauses

A while back, we discussed how adjectival and adverbial clauses can add description to a sentence. Did you know, however, that these clauses can be either *nonrestrictive* or *restrictive*?

A **nonrestrictive phrase** or **clause** adds information to a sentence that may be interesting but is not essential to the meaning of the sentence. To determine whether a phrase or clause is nonrestrictive, remove it from the sentence. If the meaning does not change, the phrase or clause is nonrestrictive.

I winced, *wishing I had thought to move the vase before I'd left those two alone in the living room.*

A **restrictive phrase** or **clause** adds information to a sentence that is essential to its meaning. Yet unlike their counterparts, do not set off restrictive phrases and clauses from the rest of the sentence with any kind of punctuation (commas, dashes, etc.).

If you eat food *that can stain the carpet*, please stay in the kitchen.

Notice how the meaning of the sentence changes if we remove the restrictive clause:

If you eat food, please stay in the kitchen.

Remember, adjectival clauses usually begin with a **relative pronoun**, such as *who, whoever, which* or *that*. Adverbial clauses often begin with a **subordinating conjunction**.

Exercises

1. The following instructions have to do with the first sentence in the second paragraph.

   a. We believe the author mis-punctuated the sentence. It seems as though the sentence includes a nonrestrictive phrase, but the author failed to set it off with commas. Please add commas where they belong, and circle the commas you add.

   b. If the nonrestrictive clause is set off appropriately, it should be clear that the original comma is wholly unnecessary. Put an arrow over the comma you no longer need.

2. Do the words **The whale plunged** form a phrase or a clause?   **Phrase**   **Clause**

3. Draw brackets around the simple sentences.

4. **Challenge:** What is true about the second sentence? (Check all that apply.)

   ☐ **It is a simple sentence**   ☐ **It has a simple subject**

   ☐ **It is a compound sentence**   ☐ **It has a compound predicate**

   ☐ **It has a compound subject**   ☐ **It has a simple predicate**

5. What kind of sentence is the last one?

   Imperative   **Interrogative**   **Exclamatory**   **Declarative**

6. Analyze the second paragraph.

Grammar 5: Sheet 43

Passage

The Incredible Journey, p. 19:

Twenty minutes passed by and no move was made; then suddenly the young dog rose, stretched himself, and stood looking intently down the drive. Then slowly the Labrador walked down the driveway and stood at the curve, looking back as though inviting the others to come. The old dog rose too, now, somewhat stiffly, and followed. Together they turned the corner, out of sight.

Exercises

1. Put boxes around any compound words, then use slashes to divide them into their parts.

2. Use slashes to divide **twenty**, **minutes**, **suddenly**, **stretched**, and **others** into syllables.

3. **Looking**, and **inviting** are participles. Rewrite the second sentence and replace the participles with true action verbs.

   _____

   _____

   _____

   _____

4. The author wrote the first clause in the passive voice. Please rewrite it in the active voice.

   _____

   _____

5. Write the person (first, second, third) and number (singular, plural) of the pronoun in the final sentence.

   _____   _____

6. Write **cc** above any coordinating conjunctions and **sc** above any subordinating conjunctions.

7. Analyze the last two sentences.

This page intentionally left blank.

Grammar 5: Sheet 44

Passage

The Incredible Journey, pp. 25–26:

The young dog slept in fitful, uneasy starts, his muscles twitching, constantly lifting his head and growling softly. Once he sprang to his feet with a full-throated roar which brought a sudden splash in the distance, then silence—and who knows what else unknown, unseen or unheard passed through his mind to disturb him further? Only one thing was clear and certain—that at all costs he was going home, home to his own beloved master.

Exercises

1. Underline the five words that have prefixes and circle the prefixes.

2. Draw a box around the complete subject of the first sentence and write **s** above the simple subject.

3. **Twitching**, **lifting** and **growling** are participles. Rewrite the first sentence and replace the participles with action verbs.

   _____

   _____

4. Draw a squiggly line under the participial phrase in the first sentence.

   Discuss with Mom or Dad: Do you think this is a dangling participle? Why or why not?

   _____

5. Analyze the first sentence.

6. Think of two antonyms or, at least, contrastive expressions for each of the following words. Feel free to use prepositional phrases, clauses, or other longer means of expressing the opposite idea!

   young _____   **dog** _____

   uneasy _____   **constantly** _____

   softly _____   **sudden** _____

   silence _____

   master _____

7. Why is there a comma between **fitful** and **uneasy** in the first sentence?

   ☐ **Because you should always set off an introductory adverbial clause with a comma.**

   ☐ **Because you should always set off a non-restrictive appositive phrase with commas.**

   ☐ **Because you should always set off an introductory participial or prepositional phrase with a comma.**

   ☐ **Because you should always use a comma to separate adjectives that equally modify the same noun.**

   ☐ **There is no good reason for the commas.**

8. Double underline the rhetorical question.

Passage   Expletives

The Incredible Journey, p. 101:

It would have been impossible to find three more contented animals that night. They lay curled closely together in a hollow filled with sweet-scented needles, under an aged, spreading balsam tree, near the banks of the stream. The old dog had his beloved cat, warm and purring between his paws again, and he snored in deep contentment. The young dog, their gently worried leader, had found his charge again.

F.Y.I.: Expletives

In English, an **expletive** is a word or phrase that adds information to a sentence but exists only to help the sentence maintain its structure. An expletive acts as the subject or object of a verb, but needs a following word or phrase to provide the meaningful content. Often, expletives appear as the word *it* or *there* in the beginning of a sentence, followed by a form of the verb **to be**.

> *It was* a dark and stormy night when I first heard the sound.
> *There might have been* more if I hadn't dropped the plate on my way inside.

Expletives add nothing to a sentence. Since expletives act as fillers and can give your message a stuffy tone, seek to remove them from your writing.

Exercises

1. The word **it** in the first sentence is an **expletive**: it means nothing, but it takes up the space where we would expect to find a subject. This sentence has a **delayed subject**. The true subject of this sentence is the infinitive **to find**. Please rewrite the sentence so that its subject comes at the beginning. _____

   _____

   _____

   _____

2. Write **prep** above all prepositions, **op** above all objects of prepositions, and draw parentheses around all prepositional phrases.

3. Find, draw brackets around, and write **appos** above the appositive.

4. Underline the complete predicate of the final sentence.

5. Find a comparative adverb and write **comp adv** above it, then write its superlative form here: _____

_____

6. Is the first sentence a good topic sentence?

    ☐ **Yes**

    ☐ **Another would be better**

    ☐ **There really isn't a good topic sentence in the paragraph**

Why? (Discuss your answer with your mom or dad.)

Passage   Subject-Verb Agreement

Rascal, p. 26:

"It is hungry, the little one," she said, petting the small raccoon. "Go fetch a

clean wheat straw, Oscar."

She filled her own mouth with warm milk, put the wheat straw between her

lips, and slanted the straw down to the mouth of the little raccoon. I watched,

fascinated, as my new pet took the straw eagerly and began to nurse.

F.Y.I.: Subject-Verb Agreement

You already know that nouns (or subjects) can either be singular or plural, but did you know that verbs can
be too?

The boys eats quickly.

We're confident you know the above sentence contains an error, but what is wrong, specifically? Well, the subject **boys**
is a plural subject, but it's been paired with the singular form of the verb "to eat." To eliminate this **subject-verb agreement** error, the verb and the subject must agree in both *person* and *number*.

The *boy eats* quickly. (Singular subject and verb.)
The *boys eat* quickly. (Plural subject and verb.)

There are a few of special cases where subject-verb agreement follows particular rules:

Additional Rules for Subject-Verb Agreement		
Special Case:	Rule:	For Example…
Every**one**, Every**body**, **Each**	Even though they may sound plural, treat these pronouns as **singular**.	*Everyone has* left the building. *Each* of the students *is* responsible.
and	This conjunction creates a compound subject—the verb should be plural	Harry *and* I *eat* our lunches under the tree.
Neither, Either	These pronouns are singular and require singular verbs.	Either *is* fine with me.
or, nor	When these words are used, the subject closest to the verb determines the number.	Either David or *the girls run* the forklift. Either the girls or *David runs* the forklift.
It, Here, There	These words are never subjects! (Remember expletives?) The delayed subject determines the number of the verb.	There *are* three *chickens* over here. There *is* a *chicken* over here.
Finally, be careful to not let modifiers that lie between the subject and the verb confuse the agreement between the two: *Brian,* who with dramatic flair swept the contents of his locker into his bag, and without looking back, turned to flee in the company of his friends, *is* finally done with school.		

⇨ **Sheet 46** *Continued...*

In two special cases, it can be tricky to determine subject-verb agreement:

1. **Collective nouns take singular verbs** because you're talking about only "one" group:

   Yes: My family *loves* to read. (One family = singular)
   No: My family *love* to read.

2. **Proper names that include a plural noun also take singular verbs** because the whole proper noun refers to one item.

   Yes: I have heard that <u>Holes</u> *is* a great movie. (One movie = singular)
   No: I have heard that <u>Holes</u> *are* a great movie.

Exercises

1. Rewrite the following to eliminate the agreement errors.

   The children sleeps in the red room. _____

   _____

   My cat jump to and hang from the blinds all the time. _____

   _____

   When the bell rings, the class quiet and wait patiently. _____

   _____

   Jacob always run to practice after school. _____

   _____

2. What is the tense of the linking verb in the first sentence? **Past** **Present** **Future**

   What is the tense of the active verb in the first sentence? **Past** **Present** **Future**

3. Write **nda** above the noun of direct address.

   What are you supposed to do when you write a noun of direct address? (Circle all that apply.)

   Capitalize it   **Use commas to set it off**   **Make sure it comes at the beginning or end of the sentence**

4. Underline the complex sentence and write **sc** above the subordinating conjunction.

5. Put a check mark above the possessive pronouns.

6. Analyze the first sentence of both paragraphs. Skip the phrase **petting the small raccoon**.

7. Should there be a paragraph break after "small raccoon" in the first paragraph? **Yes** **No**

   Why or why not? _____

   _____

   _____

Passage

Rascal, p. 33:

Rascal felt the lump of sugar, sniffed it, and then began his usual washing ceremony, swishing it back and forth through his bowl of milk. In a few moments, of course, it melted entirely away, and a more surprised little 'coon you have never seen in your life. He looked at me and trilled a shrill question: who had stolen his sugar lump?

F.Y.I.: Indirect Quotations

Sometimes, somebody may tell you what someone else said, but not relay the message word-for-word.

Usually, this kind of communication is fine, as long as the message doesn't change (and you know, for example, that Mom said to come for dinner *now* rather than "when you feel like it")! In literature, if an author modifies a quotation in any way, the quotation is then called an **indirect quotation**. This type of quotation is not set apart by quotation marks. Consider the following:

> Bubba hollered up the stairs, "We need to purchase another mouse trap, honey!"

And the author wrote:

> Bubba hollered up the stairs that we needed to purchase another mouse trap.

Even though the author's version simply changed the tense of verb *need* to *needed* and omitted the noun of direct address in Bubba's message, the quotation is no longer a direct quote.

The same would be true if we simply modified a pronoun.

> "I need to pick up a new mouse trap!"
> We need to pick up a new mouse trap.

Exercises

1. Underline the indirect quote.

2. What is the structure of the first sentence?

   Simple   **Compound**   **Complex**   **Compound-Complex**

   What is the structure of the second sentence?

   Simple   **Compound**   **Complex**   **Compound-Complex**

   What is the structure of the last sentence?

   Simple   **Compound**   **Complex**   **Compound-Complex**

⇨ **Sheet 47** *Continued...*

3. Overall, what is the tense of this paragraph?   **Past**   **Present**   **Future**

4. Write **part** above the participles **washing** and **surprised**. Draw arrows to the nouns or pronouns they modify.

5. Double underline the parenthetical expression.

6. Analyze the second sentence. **Hint**: **'coon** is a direct object.

    For what verb is **'coon** a direct object?   **melted**   **surprised**   **seen**

Grammar 5: Sheet 48

Passage

Rascal, p. 118:

Rascal loved holes of all sizes, from crayfish holes to be explored with a sensitive paw, to holes such as this one, big enough to crawl into. While I put fresh straw in the box stall, and enclosed it in chicken wire, my raccoon spent most of his time going in and out of his pleasant little door.

Exercises

1. Draw brackets around each clause in the second sentence. Mark any independent clauses with **ind** and any dependent clauses with **dep**.

   The first clause has what type of predicate?   **Simple**   **Compound**   **Complete**

   Why? _____

   _____

2. Why is there a comma after **chicken wire**?

   ☐ **Because you should always set off parenthetical comments with commas.**

   ☐ **Because you should always set off introductory dependent clauses with commas.**

   ☐ **The comma really isn't necessary.**

   ☐ **Because you should always set off interjections with commas or exclamation points.**

   ☐ **Because you should always set off a nonrestrictive phrase or clause with commas.**

3. Write **inf** above the infinitives.

4. Underline the word that has a prefix and circle the prefix.

5. Analyze the last sentence up to, but not including, the gerund **going**.

6. Rewrite the first sentence as two or more sentences. _____

   _____

   _____

7. How many kinds of holes can you think of? See if you can think of six different types of holes.

   _____

   _____

   _____

This page intentionally left blank.

Passage

Rascal, pp. 160–161:

How could anyone mutilate the sensitive, questing hands of an animal like Rascal? I picked up my raccoon and hugged him in a passion of remorse.

I burned my fur catalogues in the furnace and hung my traps in the loft of the barn, never to use them again. Men had stopped killing other men in France that day; and on that day I signed a permanent peace treaty with the animals and the birds. It is perhaps the only peace treaty that was ever kept.

F.Y.I.: More Types of Pronouns

We have already discussed several types of **pronouns**. Today, we'll learn about a few more types that you'll probably recognize.

Demonstrative pronouns are used to point out particular people or things. There are only four demonstrative pronouns: *this, these, that, those.*

> Did you use *this* eraser?

Indefinite pronouns are undefined—there is something about them that we do not know. Usually, we don't know exactly to whom or what they refer. They include: *anyone, someone, all, most, everyone, everything,* etc.

> Did *anyone* buy milk today?

Reflexive pronouns refer (or reflect) back to the subject of a sentence. Reflexive pronouns include: *myself, yourself, himself, itself,* etc. **Note:** "hisself" and "theirselves" are not real words!

> He tied his shoe *himself.*

Intensive pronouns are exactly the same as reflexive pronouns, except they are used to *emphasize* another noun or pronoun instead of referring back to it.

> Intensive: My boss *himself* delivered the cookies.
> Reflexive: My boss delivered the cookies *himself.*

Interrogative pronouns are used in questions.

> *Which* restaurant shall we visit?

The table on the back side of this sheet compares and gives further examples of each of these types of pronouns.

Exercises

1. Write **s** above the simple subject of the first sentence. What kind of word is it?

An intensive pronoun   **An indefinite pronoun**   **An interrogative pronoun**   **A demonstrative pronoun**

2. Write **n** above the nouns and draw asterisks above the proper nouns.

3. What is the person (first, second, third) and number (singular, plural) of the first word of the second paragraph?

    _____   _____

4. What is the tense of **men had stopped killing**?

    Simple past   **Continuing past**   **Past perfect**

5. Analyze the first paragraph. **Hint:** The word **How**, here, is an adverb.

6. Mr. North used two adjectives to describe the hands of an animal like Rascal. Please come up with at least four other adjectives you might use to describe **hands** (any hands—yours, someone else's, Rascal's, etc.).

    _____

    _____

    _____

Additional Types of Pronouns				
Type:	Description:	Singular:	Plural:	Example:
Demonstrative	Refers to things nearby	this	these	*This* is my chair.
	Refers to things far away	that	those	Let's run to *those* trees.
Indefinite	We don't know exactly to whom or what they refer.	anybody, anyone, anything, each, either, everybody, everyone, everything, neither, nobody, no one, nothing, one, somebody, someone, something	both, few, many, several	I don't know *anyone* who can drive.
		Singular or Plural: all, any, most, some		
Reflexive	Refer back to the subject of a sentence.	myself, yourself, himself, herself, itself	ourselves, yourselves, themselves	I paid for the ticket *myself.*
Intensive	Used to emphasize another noun or pronoun	myself, yourself, himself, herself, itself	ourselves, yourselves, themselves	He *himself* broke the pencil.
Relative	Connect nouns or pronouns to phrases or clauses (such as adjectival clauses)	that, which, who, whom, whose, whichever, whoever, whomever		Andy, *who* climbed a mountain last year, can eat like a horse.
Interrogative	Used in questions	what, who, which, whom, whose		*Which* team members will come to the party?

Grammar 5: Sheet 50

Just So Stories, p. 18:

'Do you see that?' said the Djinn. 'That's your very own humph that you've brought upon your very own self by not working. Today is Thursday, and you've done no work since Monday, when the work began. Now you are going to work.'

F.Y.I.: Parallel Structure

     A sentence contains **parallel structure** when the same pattern of words is used repeatedly to show that multiple ideas have the same level of importance. Usually, <u>coordinating conjunctions</u> join parallel structures. For example:

        Austin likes *to hike*, *to swim*, <u>and</u> *to play* hockey.

Parallel structure can also appear as clauses:

        Our youth pastor told us *that we should* get plenty of rest, *that we should* bring a sack lunch, <u>and</u> *that we should* leave our headphones at home on the day we left for our trip.

In order for the structure to be parallel, all elements must stay in the same form. Here are a few examples that are not parallel, due to the change in form.

        Please finish the test quick*ly*, accurate*ly*, and ***in the required amount of time***.
        In my swimming class, you will learn breath*ing*, kick*ing*, pull*ing* and ***proper stroke techniques***.

Exercises

1. Find the parallel expression in the second sentence. Please underline both halves of the parallelism.

 Why do you think the Djinn uses the parallelism? _____

 _____

 _____

2. Draw brackets around each clause in the second sentence. Mark any independent clauses with **ind** and any dependent clauses with **dep**.

 Therefore, what is the structure of this sentence?   **Simple**   **Compound**   **Complex**   **Compound-Complex**

3. Draw brackets around each clause in the third sentence. Mark any independent clauses with **ind** and any dependent clauses with **dep**.

 Therefore, what is the structure of this sentence?   **Simple**   **Compound**   **Complex**   **Compound-Complex**

4. What type of sentence is the first quoted sentence?

     Imperative   **Interrogative**   **Exclamatory**   **Declarative**

⇨

What type of sentence is the last one?

Imperative   **Interrogative**   **Exclamatory**   **Declarative**

5. The gerund **working** is a noun. What is its grammatical function? _____

   _____

   _____

6. Analyze the third sentence.

Grammar 5: Sheet 51

Passage

Just So Stories, p. 111:

Some day men will call it writing. At present it is only pictures, and, as we have seen today, pictures are not always properly understood. But a time will come, O Babe of Tegumai, when we shall make letters—all twenty-six of 'em,—and when we shall be able to read as well as to write, and then we shall always say exactly what we mean without any mistakes.

Exercises

1. Draw an arrow that points to the hyphen. What is it used for?

   ☐ **To form an adjective**

   ☐ **To create a compound word**

   ☐ **To show that something is missing**

   ☐ **To avoid confusion or awkward spelling**

   ☐ **To create a new word**

   ☐ **To create a compound number between twenty-one and ninety-nine**

   ☐ **There is no good reason to include a hyphen**

2. Draw parentheses around and write **appos** above the appositive phrase.

3. Write **inf** above any infinitives.

4. Write **nda** above the noun of direct address.

5. Underline any words that have suffixes. Write the original root words here:

   _____   _____

   _____   _____

   _____   _____

   _____   _____

6. **Challenge: Men** and **understood** have been modified without suffixes. Write their root words here:

   _____   _____

7. What is the tense of the first sentence?   **Past**   **Present**   **Future**

8. What is the structure of the first sentence?

    Simple   **Compound**   **Complex**   **Compound-Complex**

    What is the structure of the second sentence?

    Simple   **Compound**   **Complex**   **Compound-Complex**

    What is the structure of the third sentence?

    Simple   **Compound**   **Complex**   **Compound-Complex**

9. Analyze the second sentence.

10. The author wrote the last clause in the second sentence in the passive voice. Please rewrite it in the active voice.

    _____

    _____

    _____

Passage

Just So Stories, p. 177:

> "Ah," said the Woman, listening, "this is a very clever Cat, but he is not so
>
> clever as my Man."

F.Y.I.: Interjections

An **interjection** is a one- or two-word expression of strong emotion or surprise. Interjections often end with an exclamation point, or may be set apart from the rest of a sentence with commas.

Ah, how I love summertime.
Wow! Is that the score of the game?
Oh! Would you also pick up dessert on your way home?

Exercises

1. Write **int** above the interjection and **part/adj** above the participle.

2. Draw an arrow from **he** to its antecedent.

3. Draw brackets around each clause. Mark any independent clauses with **ind** and any dependent clauses with **dep**. Therefore, what is its sentence structure?

   | Simple | Compound | Complex | Compound-Complex |

4. In the last clause, what is the case of the pronoun **he**?

   | Nominative | Possessive | Objective |

5. Analyze the sentence up to, but not including, **as my Man**. **Note:** the participle serves as an adjective to describe the **Woman**.

6. Rewrite the sentence in such a way that the attribution comes in a different spot. _____

   _____

   _____

   _____

7. Write synonyms for the following words. Of course you may use prepositional phrases or participles if they work!

   said _____   **listening** _____

   very _____   **clever** _____

This page intentionally left blank.

Grammar 5: Sheet 53

Passage

Around the World in Eighty Days, p. 14:

"Upon my word," said Passepartout to himself, "I have known at Madame Tussaud's good people as lively as my new master!"

It is proper to say here that Madame Tussaud's "good people" are wax figures, much visited in London, and who, indeed, are only wanting in speech.

Exercises

1. Write **int** above the interjection.

   Write two new interjections. _____

   _____

2. Underline the simile in today's passage.

3. Passepartout, we are told, speaks **to himself**. Depending on the context in which it is used, **himself** is a reflexive or intensive pronoun. Which is it here?

   Reflexive   **Intensive**

   Suppose Passepartout had said, **I myself have known at Madame Tussaud's good people as lively as my new master!** Would **myself**, in that context, be a reflexive or intensive pronoun?

   Reflexive   **Intensive**

   Write four other reflexive or intensive pronouns (other than **himself** and **myself**).

   _____   _____

   _____   _____

4. **Visited** and **wanting** are participles. Rewrite the last clause to replace these participles with verbs.

   _____

   _____

5. Analyze the first sentence up to, but not including, **as lively as my new master**.

6. According to the passage, what is the only thing the wax figurines at Madame Tussaud's lack? _____

   _____

   _____

This page intentionally left blank.

Passage

Around the World in Eighty Days, p. 24:

"Heaven preserve me!" exclaimed Stuart, "but I would willingly wager four thousand pounds that such a journey, made under these conditions, is impossible."

"On the contrary, quite possible," replied Mr. Fogg.

"Well, make it, then!"

"The tour of the world in eighty days?"

"Yes!"

"I am willing."

Exercises

1. Write **int** above any interjections and put brackets around the parenthetical expression.

2. Find and write all words that have prefixes or suffixes, then rewrite them in their root forms.

_____ _____   _____ _____

_____ _____   _____ _____

_____ _____   _____ _____

_____ _____   _____ _____

_____ _____   _____ _____

3. Underline the three sentence fragments.

4. Write the sentence fragments as complete sentences.

_____

_____

_____

_____

_____

5. Think of two antonyms or, at least, contrastive expressions for each of the following words. Feel free to use prepositional phrases, clauses, or other longer means of expressing the opposite idea!

   heaven _____ **preserve** _____

   under _____ **contrary** _____

   wager _____ **impossible** _____

6. Analyze the first sentence. **Hint:** The word **made** is a participle.

Grammar 5: Sheet 55

Passage

Around the World in Eighty Days, pp. 51–52:

No one is ignorant of the fact that India, this great reversed triangle whose base is to the north and its apex to the south, comprises a superficial area of fourteen hundred thousand square miles, over which is unequally scattered a population of one hundred and eighty millions of inhabitants.

Exercises

1. Write **prep** above all prepositions, **op** above all objects of prepositions, and draw parentheses around all prepositional phrases.

2. Write **part** above the participles **reversed** and **scattered**. Draw arrows to the nouns they modify.

3. Underline the appositive phrase.

4. Write a homophone for each of the following words.

   great _____   **one** _____

   whose _____   **its** _____

   eight _____   **which** _____

5. Analyze the clause **No one is ignorant of the fact**. If you find a prepositional phrase, please surround it with parentheses.

6. Describe the same triangle in your own words.

   _____

   _____

   _____

   _____

   _____

   _____

   _____

   _____

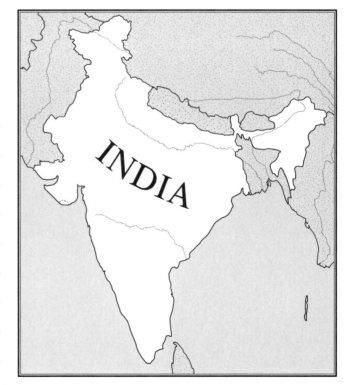

This page intentionally left blank.

Passage

Around the World in Eighty Days, p. 71:

"A suttee, Mr. Fogg," replied the brigadier-general, "is a human sacrifice, but a voluntary sacrifice. The woman that you have just seen will be burned tomorrow in the early part of the day."

F.Y.I.: Attribution

You probably already know that an **attribution** is the phrase that indicates who said whatever is being quoted. Attributions can be placed before, in the middle of, or after a quotation. Let's discuss some of the nuances of attributions to help you write them correctly.

When the attribution appears before a quotation, name the speaker, follow that with a comma, and then state the quotation.

Bo said, "Where shall we go for lunch?"

When the attribution lies in the middle of a sentence, we set the attribution off with commas.

"I emailed the file to you," *said Duane,* "and will put the books in the mail today."

When the attribution falls between two sentences of a quote, attach the attribution to the sentence that comes before it, and separate it with a comma. **Note:** the comma should lie on the inside of the closing quotation mark.

"Here is a box for you," *said Nate.* "I can help you carry it to your car if you like."

Keep in mind that if the quoted sentence ends in an exclamation point or a question mark, keep them—don't replace them with a comma.

"That's the best thing I've heard in a long time!" *exclaimed Duane.*
"Can you believe it?" *Amber asked.*

Finally, you should start a new paragraph whenever a new speaker begins to talk in a dialog. Once you have identified the characters, however, you don't have to include attributions in every line. The change in paragraphs is enough for the reader to understand that two characters are speaking back and forth.

"Is that dinosaur going to eat us?" *gasped Amber.*
"No," *sighed Bubba,* "That's a friendly one."
"How can you tell?"
"He's wearing a name tag."

Exercises

1. Rewrite the first sentence so that the attribution moves and the quotation itself is simpler. _____

_____

_____

2. Write **n** above the nouns.

⇨ **Sheet 56** *Continued...*

3. Use slashes to divide **general, human, sacrifice, voluntary, woman, tomorrow,** and **early** into syllables.

4. What is the tense of the verb **replied** in the first sentence?

    Past Perfect   **Past**   **Present Perfect**   **Present**

    What is the tense of the verb phrase **have just seen**?

    Past Perfect   **Present Perfect**   **Present**   **Future**

    What is the tense of the verb phrase **will be burned**?

    Past   **Past Perfect**   **Present**   **Future**

5. Analyze the paragraph.

6. Write a sentence in which **brigadier-general** should be capitalized. _____

    _____

    _____

Grammar 5: Sheet 57

Passage

Around the World in Eighty Days, p. 86:

According to his journal, this gentleman should arrive in the capital of India, October 25, twenty-three days after leaving London, and he arrived there on the stipulated day. He was neither behind nor ahead of time. Unfortunately, the two days gained by him between London and Bombay had been lost—we know how—in this trip across the Indian peninsula, but it is to be supposed that Phileas Fogg did not regret them.

Exercises

1. Write **prep** above all prepositions, **op** above all objects of prepositions, and draw parentheses around all prepositional phrases.

2. Write **part** above the participles **stipulated** and **gained**, and draw arrows from the participles to the nouns or pronouns they modify.

   The word **leaving** is what? (Check all that apply)

   ☐ **A participle**   ☐ **A direct object**   ☐ **An object of a preposition**

   ☐ **A gerund**   ☐ **A predicate adjective**   ☐ **A noun**

3. Draw an arrow that points to the hyphen.

   What is the hyphen used for? (Check all that apply.)

   ☐ **To form an adjective**   ☐ **To avoid confusion or awkward spelling**

   ☐ **To create a compound word**   ☐ **To create a number between twenty-one and ninety-nine**

   ☐ **To show that something is missing**   ☐ **There is no good reason to include a hyphen**

4. Circle the one word that has a prefix and a suffix. Write the root of this word here: _____

5. Analyze the last clause from the subordinating conjunction **that**.

6. Draw a box around the parenthetical expression.

   How else might the parenthetical expression be punctuated? _____

   _____

   _____

7.   Write at least three other ways you might communicate the meaning of the phrase **the stipulated day**.

_____

_____

_____

_____

Passage   Italics

Around the World in Eighty Days, pp. 106–107:

During the days of the third and fourth of November it was a sort of tempest. The squall struck the sea with violence. The *Rangoon* had to go slowly for half a day, keeping herself in motion with only ten revolutions of the screw, so as to lean with the waves. All the sails had been reefed, and there was still too much rigging whistling in the squall.

F.Y.I.: Italics

In printed materials, **italic type** (which looks slightly slanted *like this*) is used in a number of ways. Italics can identify titles of books, magazines and album titles.

> *Pride and Prejudice* is the next book I plan to read.
> Let's order *Reader's Digest* for Grandma.
> The Dave Matthews Band song "Ants Marching" is on the album *Under the Table and Dreaming*.

Italics are also used to give emphasis to a particular word or phrase.

> She was *really* excited to see me.

Italics can also identify words that are being used or discussed somehow.

> The phrase *so that* is a subordinating conjunction.

Finally, italics can help identify foreign words.

> I only had three *pesos* left after our trip to the market.

Exercises

1. Why is **Rangoon** italicized?

   ☐ **It is a parenthetical expression**

   ☐ **It is the name of the boat**

   ☐ **For emphasis**

2. Write **prep** above all prepositions, **op** above all objects of prepositions, and draw parentheses around all prepositional phrases.

3. Write **inf** above any infinitives

4. Underline the personification in the passage.

5. Analyze the second sentence and the third sentence through the word **screw**. **Hint:** Treat the words **had to go** as a single verb phrase; mark it, therefore, as **v**. Skip the phrase **keeping herself**, and remember: adverbs modify adjectives.

6. Write **part** above the participles **keeping** and **whistling**. Draw arrows from the participles or participial phrases to the nouns they modify.

7. Rewrite the last sentence and replace the participle **whistling** with a true verb. _____

_____

_____

_____

Grammar 5: Sheet 59

Passage

Around the World in Eighty Days, p. 126:

This voyage of eight hundred miles, undertaken in a craft of twenty tons, and especially in that season of the year, was venturesome. The Chinese seas are generally rough, exposed to terrible blows, principally during the equinoxes, and this was in the first days of November.

Exercises

1. Analyze the first sentence. If you find a prepositional phrase, please surround it with parentheses. **Note: undertaken** is a participle acting as an adjective.

2. Draw brackets around and write **part** above the participial phrases, **undertaken in a craft of twenty tons** and **exposed to terrible blows**. Draw an arrow to the nouns or pronouns they modify.

3. Write the root words of the following:

   miles _____   **especially** _____

   generally _____   **exposed** _____

   principally _____   **equinoxes** _____

4. Rewrite the first sentence in its simplest form (with all of the prepositions, prepositional phrases, and participial phrases removed). _____

   _____

   _____

5. The following words are all homographs. Write one additional meaning for each word.

   blows _____   **rough** _____

   exposed _____   **craft** _____

6. What adjectives could you use to communicate the idea contained in the word **venturesome**? List at least four.

   _____   _____

   _____   _____

   _____   _____

7. What is the difference between **a principal** and **a principle**?

    a principal: _____

    a principle: _____

8. **Challenge:** What are the equinoxes? _____

    _____

    When are the equinoxes? _____

    _____

    So how significant is the information that **this was in the first days of November**? _____

    _____

9. **Challenge:** How many pounds is twenty tons, if a ton is 2,000 pounds? _____

    _____

    _____

Grammar 5: Sheet 60

Passage

Around the World in Eighty Days, p. 155:

"Now," continued Fix, "Mr. Fogg seems to be returning to England? Well, I will follow him there. But henceforth it shall be my aim to clear the obstacles from his path as zealously and carefully as before I took pains to accumulate them. You see my game is changed, and it is changed because my interest desires it."

Exercises

1. Write **inf** above the infinitives.

2. Draw brackets around each clause. Mark any independent clauses with **ind** and any dependent clauses with **dep**.

3. Based on your analysis, what is the structure of the first sentence?

   Simple   **Compound**   **Complex**   **Compound-Complex**

   What is the structure of the second?

   Simple   **Compound**   **Complex**   **Compound-Complex**

   What is the structure of the third?

   Simple   **Compound**   **Complex**   **Compound-Complex**

   What is the structure of the fourth?

   Simple   **Compound**   **Complex**   **Compound-Complex**

4. Put boxes around any compound words, then use slashes to divide them into their parts.

5. The author (actually, translator) forgot to punctuate one of the interjections the way it should be. Please add the appropriate punctuation and circle it.

6. Analyze the second and fourth sentences. **Hint:** The word **changed** is a participle.

7. What is the grammatical term for words like **Now**, **Well**, and **You see** as they are used in today's dictation?

   Exclamation   **Declaration**   **Interjection**   **Dejection**   **Superlative**

8. Fix uses two words that rhyme: **aim** and **game**. Write at least five more words that rhyme with these two. Try to include at least one each that uses the same spelling pattern as each of the two pattern words.

   _____   _____

   _____   _____

   _____   _____

This page intentionally left blank.

Passage   **Alphbetization**

Around the World in Eighty Days, p. 195:

Mrs. Aouda retired into a sitting room of the station, and there, alone, she waited, thinking of Phileas Fogg, his simple and grand generosity, his quiet courage. Mr. Fogg had sacrificed his fortune, and now he was staking his life—and all this without hesitation, from a sense of duty, without words. Phileas Fogg was a hero in her eyes.

F.Y.I: Alphabetization

How many things can you think of that are in alphabetical order? Dictionaries, phone books, indices and books in a library are just some of the things that are alphabetized. Once you get a firm grip on how to **alphabetize** lists, it will help you find information in many places more quickly.

Alphabetization is the process of putting a series of words in alphabetical order (from *a* to *z*) according to the first letter of each word. If multiple words start with the same letter, compare the second letters or third letters…until you find letters that are different, and then order the words accordingly.

	this	these	those	that	ours

$$\downarrow$$

	ours	that	these	this	those

Exercises

1. Alphabetize the words in the last sentence. _____

   _____

2. Write **n** above the nouns.

3. Write **prep** above all prepositions, **op** above all objects of prepositions, and draw parentheses around all prepositional phrases.

4. Put boxes around the compound words and use slashes to divide them into the words of which they are made.

5. What is the case of **she**, the first pronoun in the passage?

   Nominative   **Objective**   **Possessive**

   What is the case of **his**, the first pronoun in the second sentence?

   Nominative   **Objective**   **Possessive**

⇨

6. What is the tense of the first clause in the second sentence?

   Past Perfect   **Simple Past**   **Continuing Present**

   What is the tense of the second clause in the same sentence?

   Simple present   **Continuing Past**   **Continuing Present**

7. Why did the author use a dash?

   ☐ **To set off a parenthetical or explanatory remark**

   ☐ **To indicate interrupted speech**

   ☐ **To emphasize the words that follow**

   ☐ **It doesn't belong there; the author should have used _____ instead**

8. Analyze the last sentence.

Grammar 5: Sheet 62

Passage

Ali and the Golden Eagle, p. 12:

Their houses were hundreds of years old, built and rebuilt from mud bricks with straw to hold them together. The stones lining the street were worn down from centuries of being walked on. The villagers had burros, sheep, and goats, and all were healthy and well fed. Almost everything was made by hand from the natural resources found in their isolated valley.

Exercises

1. Write **prep** above all prepositions, **op** above all objects of prepositions, and draw parentheses around all prepositional phrases.

2. Write **part** above the participles **built**, **rebuilt**, **lining**, **fed**, and **found**. Draw arrows that point from these participles to the nouns for which they serve as adjectives.

3. Analyze the third sentence.

4. Rewrite the second sentence in the active voice. _____

   _____

5. Mr. Grover did not write very clearly when he said the houses were **built and rebuilt from mud bricks with straw to hold *them* together**. ...to which noun does the pronoun **them** refer: the **houses** or the **bricks**? Does the straw hold the mud bricks together, or does the straw hold the houses together? Really, it makes more sense that the straw held the mud in the bricks together. Please rewrite the first sentence in such a way that you eliminate this ambiguity.

   _____

   _____

   _____

6. Is the first sentence a good topic sentence?

   ☐ **Yes**

   ☐ **Another would be better**

   ☐ **There really isn't a good topic sentence in the paragraph**

   Why? (Discuss your answer with your mom or dad.)

7. **Challenge:** What grammatical function does the gerund clause **being walked on** fulfill? _____

_____

_____

_____

Grammar 5: Sheet 63

Passage

Ali and the Golden Eagle, p. 44:

Ali, I have a surprise for you. Today we will build a way to catch an eagle baby.

I have everything we need in my Rover. Come, we have much work to do.

Exercises

1. Write **nda** above the noun of direct address.

2. Draw brackets around each clause. Mark any independent clauses with **ind** and any dependent clauses with **dep**.

3. Based on your analysis, what is the structure of the first sentence?

   Simple   **Compound**   **Complex**   **Compound-Complex**

   What is the structure of the second?

   Simple   **Compound**   **Complex**   **Compound-Complex**

   What is the structure of the third?

   Simple   **Compound**   **Complex**   **Compound-Complex**

   What is the structure of the fourth?

   Simple   **Compound**   **Complex**   **Compound-Complex**

4. Write **inf** above any infinitives.

5. Write **hv** over the helping verb(s).

6. Analyze the first and third sentences.

7. Write at least four adverbs to describe the verb **work**.

   _____   _____

   _____   _____

   _____   _____

8. Why is **Rover** capitalized?

9. Mr. Grover said that he and Ali had **much** work to do. Write at least four other adjectives (or adjectival phrases) for the noun **work**.

   _____

   _____

   _____

   _____

This page intentionally left blank.

Grammar 5: Sheet 64

Passage

Ali and the Golden Eagle, p. 72:

Ali, if we can master this bird, we will have the greatest hunter in all Arabia, perhaps in all the world. There is a long road ahead, but we will take it together.

Exercises

1. As it is used in the second sentence, what is the grammatical function of **There**? Be careful!

    A subject   **An object**   **An adverb**   **An expletive**

2. Analyze the paragraph. **Hint:** Use your answer to Question 1 to help you analyze the first clause of the second sentence.

3. Circle the superlative adjective.

    Write its comparative and root forms: _____

4. Underline the parallel structure in the first sentence.

5. Draw brackets around each clause. Mark any independent clauses with **ind** and any dependent clauses with **dep**.

6. Based on your analysis, what is the structure of the first sentence?

    Simple   **Compound**   **Complex**   **Compound-Complex**

    What is the structure of the second?

    Simple   **Compound**   **Complex**   **Compound-Complex**

7. Write a homophone for **road**. _____

8. The word **master** is a homograph. We have given you one meaning; you write another.

    master _____*verb: to overcome*_____   **master** _____

9. Rewrite the first clause of the second sentence so that the subject comes before the verb. _____

    _____

    _____

10. Are Ali and the speaker going on a trip? No, the "long road" at the end of this passage is a

    simile   **metaphor**.

    What does the "long road" really describe? _____

    _____

    _____

11. Think of at least three words or phrases you could use instead of the phrase **long road** in the clause **There is a long road ahead**. _____

   _____

   _____

   _____

Grammar 5: Sheet 65

Passage

Ali and the Golden Eagle, p. 117:

This village that had lived virtually unchanged for thousands of years was about to be hurtled into the twentieth century. And a fourteen-year-old boy from one of the most remote spots in Arabia was being catapulted into the modern world ... all because of an eagle.

Exercises

1. Draw brackets around each clause. Mark any independent clauses with **ind** and any dependent clauses with **dep**.

    What is the structure of the first sentence?

    Simple   **Compound**   **Complex**   **Compound-Complex**

    And what is the structure of the second?

    Simple   **Compound**   **Complex**   **Compound-Complex**

2. Overall, what type of paragraph is this?

    Expository   **Persuasive**   **Descriptive**   **Narrative**

3. What is the tense of the dependent clause in the first sentence?

    Simple Past   **Continuing Past**   **Past Perfect**

    What is the tense of the second sentence?

    Simple Past   **Continuing Past**   **Past Perfect**

4. Circle the ellipsis. What is its purpose here?

    To show a pause   **To show omitted words**

5. Put arrows above the hyphens.

    What are they there for? (Check all that apply.)

    ☐ **To form an adjective**   ☐ **To create a new word**

    ☐ **To create a compound word**   ☐ **There is no good reason to include a hyphen**

    ☐ **To show that something is missing**   ☐ **To create a number between twenty-one and ninety-nine**

    ☐ **To avoid confusion or awkward spelling**

6. Analyze the second sentence up to the ellipsis.

7. The author wrote this paragraph in the passive voice. Please rewrite the entire paragraph in an active voice.

    _____

    _____

    _____

    _____

    _____

    _____

    _____

    Which version do you like better—the passive or active voice?   **Passive**   **Active**

Grammar 5: Sheet 66

Passage

King of the Wind, p. 35:

Agba smothered a cry. Unmindful of his own safety, he thrust himself between Signor Achmet and the foal. He fell to his knees, lifting the tiny foal whose legs beat a tattoo in the air. With a look of triumph he pointed to the white spot on the off hind heel.

Signor Achmet's eyes narrowed. His brows came together in a black line. Agba could see him weighing the two in his mind—the white spot against the wheat ear. The good sign against the bad. The scales tipped even.

Exercises

1. Underline the possessive nouns and pronouns.

2. Circle the reflexive pronoun.

3. Write **part** above the participles **lifting** and **weighing**, then draw arrows from them to the nouns or pronouns they modify.

4. Rewrite the third sentence so that you replace the participle **lifting** with a verb. _____

   _____

   _____

5. Double underline the sentence fragment. Please rewrite it as a complete sentence. _____

   _____

   _____

6. Analyze the first, second, and last sentences of the second paragraph. If you find a prepositional phrase, please surround it with parentheses.

7. There is a punctuation error in the last sentence of the first paragraph. Please make the correction and circle it.

8. **Challenge:** What does it mean to **beat a tattoo**? _____

   _____

This page intentionally left blank.

Passage

King of the Wind, p. 44:

What did it matter if the other colts thought Sham was different? He was!

They ran to their mothers when they were hungry or in trouble. But Sham's

mother was a slim brown horseboy.

Exercises

1. Draw brackets around each clause. Mark any independent clauses with **ind** and any dependent clauses with **dep**.

2. Indicate the structure for each sentence.

First:	**Simple**	**Compound**	**Complex**	**Compound-Complex**
Second:	**Simple**	**Compound**	**Complex**	**Compound-Complex**
Third:	**Simple**	**Compound**	**Complex**	**Compound-Complex**

3. Evaluate the sentences indicated below, then circle the correct type for each:

First:	**Imperative**	**Interrogative**	**Exclamatory**	**Declarative**
Second:	**Imperative**	**Interrogative**	**Exclamatory**	**Declarative**
Third:	**Imperative**	**Interrogative**	**Exclamatory**	**Declarative**

4. The first sentence asks a question but without expecting an answer. What is that called?

   An exhortative question   **A rhetorical question**   **An arboreal question**   **An understood question**

5. Analyze the last two sentences.

6. Why is **They** italicized?   **It is a title**   **For emphasis**

7. Please rewrite the second sentence to include all information a reader needs to know what Sham **was**.

   _____

   _____

This page intentionally left blank.

Grammar 5: Sheet 68

Passage

King of the Wind, p. 122:

> "My poor boy! My poor boy!" Mistress Cockburn said over and over. Then she opened her hamper and placed a tart in Agba's hand. She gave Grimalkin a crust of Cheshire cheese cake and quickly covered the basket to hide the brightly scrubbed carrots.

Exercises

1. Write **nda** above the nouns of direct address.

2. Circle the proper nouns and write **n** above the common nouns.
   There is one noun phrase composed of two nouns, one of which is used as an adjective. Include this phrase also.

3. Draw boxes around the possessive nouns and pronouns.

4. **Scrubbed** is a participle. Draw an arrow that points from it to the noun it modifies.

5. What is the structure of the first sentence?

Simple	**Compound**	**Complex**	**Compound-Complex**

   What kind of predicate does it have?   **Simple**   **Compound**

6. What is the structure of the second sentence (the one that begins **Then she opened ...**)?

Simple	**Compound**	**Complex**	**Compound-Complex**

   What kind of predicate does it have?   **Simple**   **Compound**

7. And the third sentence? What is its structure?

Simple	**Compound**	**Complex**	**Compound-Complex**

   What kind of predicate does it have?   **Simple**   **Compound**

8. Analyze the last sentence through the word **basket**.

9. Ms. Henry says Mistress Cockburn covered the basket **quickly**. Please think of and write at least three other adverbs or adverbial phrases or clauses Ms. Henry could have used to describe the manner in which Mistress Cockburn covered the basket. Make sure you include at least one phrase or clause. (Remember: prepositional phrases can serve as adverbs!) _____

_____

_____

This page intentionally left blank.

Grammar 5: Sheet 69

Passage

Louis Braille, p. 15:

People sounded different too. One man had a deep cough. Another had the habit of whistling through his teeth. A third man walked with a limp. "Don't you see?" Louis felt like saying. "There are so many ways to tell people apart—if only you listen!"

Exercises

1. Write **prep** above all prepositions, **op** above all objects of prepositions, and draw parentheses around all prepositional phrases. **Hint:** The word **like** in the next-to-last sentence is a preposition.

2. Since **like** is a preposition, what is the word **saying**?

   A verb   **A participle**   **A gerund**   **An infinitive**

3. Underline the interrogative sentence.

4. What type of sentence is the last one?

   Imperative   **Interrogative**   **Exclamatory**   **Declarative**

5. Analyze the first through third sentences.

6. What is the tense of the last sentence?   **Past**   **Present**   **Future**

7. What is the person (first, second, or third) of Louis' quote?   **First**   **Second**   **Third**

8. Rewrite the third sentence to eliminate the gerund **whistling**.

9. Discuss with Mom or Dad: Is the first sentence a good topic sentence?

   ☐ **Yes**

   ☐ **No**

   ☐ **Another would be better**

   ☐ **There really isn't a good topic sentence in the paragraph**

   Why? _____

10. Circle the homophones of: **two, won, threw, sea, their, sew, weighs, yew.**

This page intentionally left blank.

Grammar 5: Sheet 70

Passage

Star of Light, p. 93:

Hamid faced the little boy shyly. "I'm from the country," he said.

"Why have you come to town?" asked the boy.

"To find work."

"Where are your mother and father?"

"Dead."

"Where do you live?"

"In the street."

Exercises

1. Write **frag** above the sentence fragments.

2. Rewrite the sentence fragments as complete sentences. _____

   _____

   _____

   _____

3. Do you think the book would be better if these fragments were written as complete sentences?   **Yes**   **No**

4. In the space available beside each unattributed quotation, please write an attribution. You may place the attribution either before or after the quotation. If you need to change a period to a comma, do so. See if you can provide enough variety in your attributions so that the dialog will feel fresh and vibrant.

   Once you have written all your attributions: do you think the passage is better for the attributions? **Yes**   **No**

5. Hamid, we are told, **faced the little boy shyly**. Please think of at least four other adverbs you could use to describe how Hamid could have faced the little boy. Make sure you include at least one prepositional phrase.

   _____   _____

   _____   _____

   _____   _____

6. What does it mean to live **in the street**? _____

   _____

7. Analyze the first two sentences.

This page intentionally left blank.

Passage

Star of Light, p. 123:

"It's the Feast of the Christians today," explained the nurse to the wide-eyed little boys, "so I thought we would keep it together. It is the Feast of the birth of Jesus Christ. He was the greatest gift God ever gave, so at His Feast we all give presents to each other. That is why Kinza has a rubber ball, and that is why I've bought you sweets and oranges and bananas."

Exercises

1. Write **n** above the common nouns and place check marks above the proper nouns. Do not count as nouns those nouns that are being used as adjectives.

2. Write **prep** above all prepositions, **op** above all objects of prepositions, and draw parentheses around all prepositional phrases.

3. Please copy the contractions in the spaces below, then write the original words for which they stand.

   _____   _____

4. Underline the parallel phrases in the passage.

5. Draw an arrow that points to the hyphen.
   Why is it there? (Check all that apply.)

   ☐ **To form an adjective**   ☐ **To create a new word**

   ☐ **To create a compound word**   ☐ **There is no good reason to include a hyphen**

   ☐ **To show that something is missing**   ☐ **To create a number between twenty-one and ninety-nine**

   ☐ **To avoid confusion or awkward spelling**

6. Please list the seven coordinating conjunctions. _____

   _____

   Use **cc** to label them in the passage.

7. Analyze the first sentence.

8. Suppose the entire phrase **Feast of the birth of Jesus Christ** was considered the name or title of the feast. How would you write the phrase? In other words, what words would you capitalize? Write them here:

   _____

⇨ **Sheet 71** *Continued...*

9. What is the common name for the **Feast of the birth of Jesus Christ**?

    _____

    Why do you think the lady doesn't use that word?

    _____

    _____

    _____

Grammar 5: Sheet 72

Passage

Star of Light, pp. 161–162:

"How does the light get into the empty lantern?" asked Rosemary. "It's just a matter of opening a door and placing a candle inside. Jesus is the Light, and He wants to come in; and we, by believing, open the door and ask Him in. Then, if the glass of the lantern is clean, the light shines out clearly; but if the glass is clouded and dirty the light will be very dim."

Exercises

1. Why do we find semicolons in the middle of the third and fourth sentences? (Check all that apply.)

   ☐ **To help join two independent clauses in one sentence—especially when they are long or contain commas**

   ☐ **To separate groups that contain commas**

   ☐ **To serve the kind of function that a period does when a comma would do; to provide a more substantial break than a comma would**

   ☐ **It shouldn't be there; the author should have used _____ instead**

2. What is the structure of the first sentence (including the attribution)?

   | **Simple** | **Compound** | **Complex** | **Compound-Complex** |

   What is the structure of the second?

   | **Simple** | **Compound** | **Complex** | **Compound-Complex** |

   What is the structure of the third?

   | **Simple** | **Compound** | **Complex** | **Compound-Complex** |

   What is the structure of the fourth?

   | **Simple** | **Compound** | **Complex** | **Compound-Complex** |

3. What are the tenses of the following clauses?

   | If the glass is clouded and dirty... | **Past** | **Present** | **Future** |

   | ...the light will be very dim... | **Past** | **Present** | **Future** |

4. Double underline the interrogative sentence.

5. Circle the antecedent to the pronoun **It** in the second sentence.

⇨ **Sheet 72** *Continued...*

6. Think of two antonyms or, at least, contrastive expressions for each of the following words. Feel free to use prepositional phrases, clauses, or other longer means of expressing the opposite idea!

    empty _____   _____

    open _____   _____

    light _____   _____

    Aunt _____   _____

    inside _____   _____

    him _____   _____

    clearly _____   _____

    clean _____   _____

7. The last sentence includes a strong example of parallelism. Please underline the parallels and draw two-headed arrows that connect the parallel phrases.

8. Analyze the third sentence.

9. Rewrite the second sentence in such a way that you eliminate the gerunds **opening** and **placing**.

    _____

    _____

    _____

    _____

My Notes

My Notes

My Notes

My Notes

My Notes

My Notes